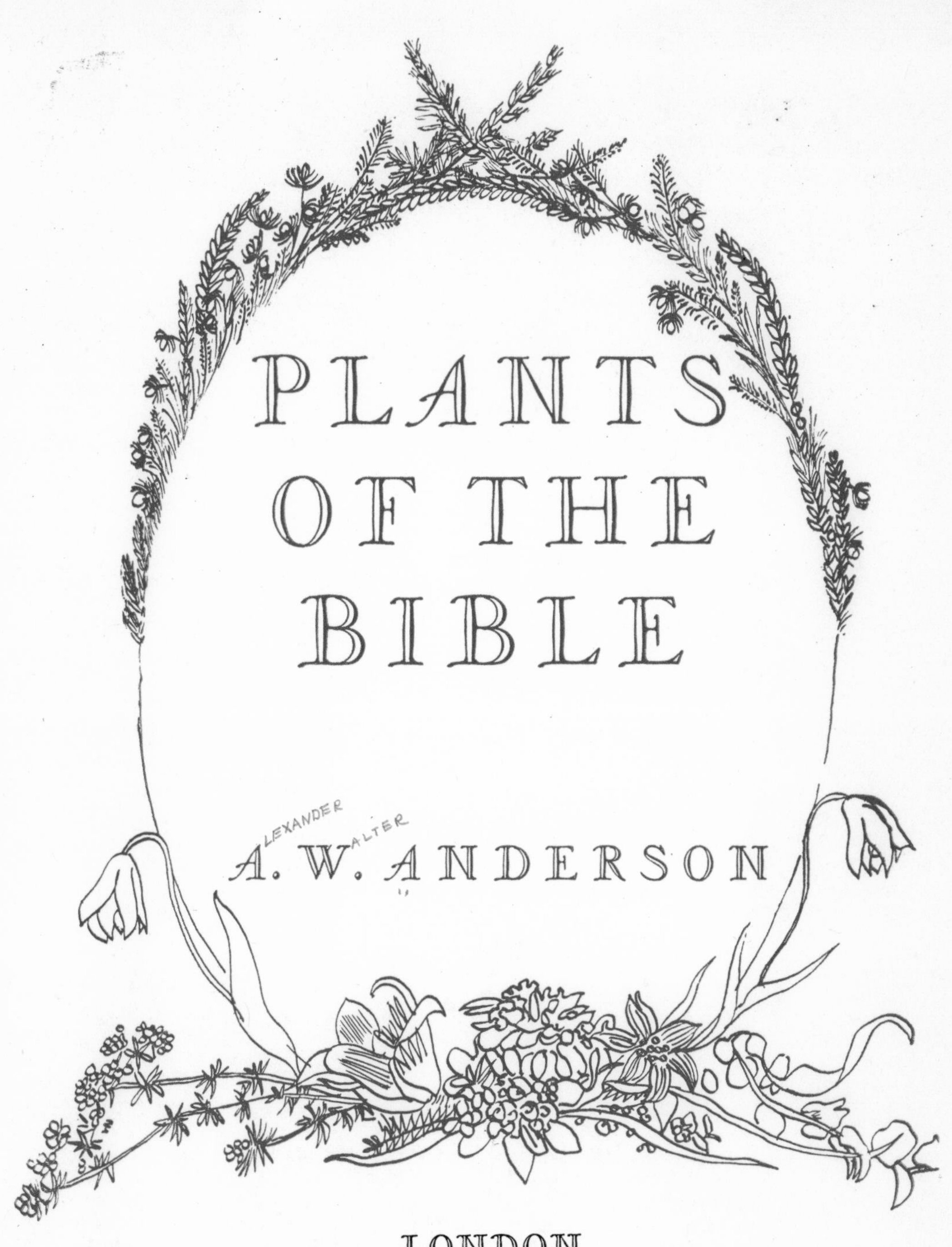

PLANTS OF THE BIBLE

A. W. ANDERSON

LONDON
CROSBY LOCKWOOD & SON LTD
26 OLD BROMPTON ROAD SW7

PRINTED AND MADE IN GREAT BRITAIN BY
FLETCHER AND SON LTD, NORWICH AND
THE LEIGHTON-STRAKER BOOKBINDING CO LTD, LONDON
COLOUR PLATES PRINTED BY
L. VAN LEER & CO., N.V., AMSTERDAM, HOLLAND

PREFACE

THE IDENTITY OF MANY BIBLE PLANTS IS SHROUDED IN THE DARKNESS OF THE PAST AND although we get a certain amount of light from the oldest botany books to come down to us,—those of Theophrastus, which were written about 300 B.C.—and John Gerard's *Herball* published in 1597 when the Authorized Version was taking shape, finality is never likely to be reached. When the plant lover brings botanical science to his aid he is not challenging the truth of the Scriptures, merely the obvious errors and inaccuracies that have crept in through human imperfection and incomplete knowledge of biblical plants.

Those who favour the idea of literal inspiration will probably find it easy to believe that the Divine method of expression would naturally use those plants and plant materials best known to the people to whom the message was originally addressed. Therefore, the true identity of the plants, trees and flowers should give a greater understanding of the Scriptures and their message.

Many books have been consulted but it is impossible to list all of them. Besides the two already mentioned I should like to acknowledge the value of Dr Post's *Flora of Syria, Palestine and Sinai*, which was adopted as the botanical authority, and Canon Tristram's *Natural History of Palestine*. H. M. and A. L. Moldenke's *Plants of the Bible*, published by Chronica Botanica, deserves special mention as the outstanding contribution to our knowledge of a most interesting subject.

At first the publishers and I had hoped to illustrate in colour each of the plants about which I have written, but the difficulty of confining my selection to twelve proved impossible and unnecessarily restricting. While it would have been pleasant to have illustrated each of the selected plants I have described, the resultant book would have been unduly expensive. This restriction of illustration has allowed us to select the more interesting paintings from a number of now rare books with which many readers may not be familiar.

My grateful thanks are due to Mr W. T. Stearn, of the Natural History Museum, South Kensington, for his advice and assistance in the selection of illustrations.

A. W. ANDERSON
ASSOCIATE OF HONOUR, ROYAL INSTITUTE
OF HORTICULTURE, NEW ZEALAND

TO THE MEMORY OF

A.M.C.

CONTENTS

LIST OF COLOUR PLATES

INTRODUCTION

APART ALTOGETHER FROM ITS SIGNIFICANCE TO THE CHRISTIAN RELIGION, THE BIBLE holds a great interest for us because it tells so much about the every-day life, customs and beliefs of a people whose world has long since passed away. From the beginning of Genesis to the end of Revelations, writings that were slowly accumulated over a long period, certainly not less than a thousand years, the trees, plants and flowers of the countryside are constantly being referred to. They formed an essential part of the life of the ancient Jews and the Bible, without its vineyards, olive groves and palm trees, its lilies, roses and other plants would be much less interesting and would lose much of its contact with the life of the ordinary man.

The plants of the Bible are mostly those of Palestine but include a few from the wilderness of Sinai and some from Egypt. The latter are mostly cultivated plants and include beans, cucumbers, onions and leeks. Ever since crusading times lilies, tulips, hyacinths and other plants from Palestine have been finding their way into our gardens and thus it is that many of the plants and flowers that grow around our homes are direct links with the lands and peoples of the Bible. We pass them every day without realizing that they are the same sorts that the Jewish spies saw when they reached the Promised Land and found it a 'land flowing with milk and honey'. Some have been changed through centuries of cultivation but many have come down to us quite unchanged since the days when they grew in King Solomon's garden, were alluded to by the prophets of old and admired by Christ who used them to illustrate his parables.

There is nothing new in this interest in Bible plants. The first book on the subject, *Herbarum atque Arborum quae in Biblis ...*, was published by L. Lemmens in 1566. He was a Dutch physician, a botanist of sorts and friendly with some of the leading botanical figures of the day, but there was no such thing as botanical classification in those days and he did little more than gather together some of the ideas of his time. For many years after the Reformation writers had to base all their conclusions, on any matter connected with Holy Scripture, on the study of comparative philology, etymology, on the internal evidence of the Bible itself, and especially in the opinions of the 'Church Fathers'.

By the middle of the eighteenth century many of these conclusions were wearing rather thin, botanists were finding difficulty in reconciling the various translations current in the Protestant countries of northern Europe and in 1773, Linnaeus, the great Swedish botanist, was given the task of identifying the plants of the Bible. He sent two of his pupils out to study the natural history of the Near East and spent a great deal of time on the subject but the few alterations he was able to induce the Swedish Commissioners to accept were not worth the effort. No one else seems to have taken any notice of his work. By that time our own Authorized Version had long since been accepted and had become 'set', and most biblical scholars took little interest in what they seem to have regarded as details of minor importance.

The leisurely days of the nineteenth century allowed many British clergymen to visit the Holy Land and there it was brought home to them that the Authorized Version contains a number of errors in its plant references, mostly brought about through mistaken identity or mis-translation. In Genesis 30: 37, for example, we are told that 'Jacob took him rods of green poplar, and of the hazel and chestnut tree', but the hazel, although admittedly found wild in a few cool mountainous parts of the country is very rare and unlikely to have been the plant referred to. Many authorities think the Oriental Plane, *Platanus orientalis*, was meant. There is no doubt about the chestnut, it is not a native of Palestine and would not have been growing there in Jacob's time, so the tree may have been the almond, but probably the white poplar, *P. alba*.

Because those early writers and translators were more interested in the theology and in the spiritual message of the Bible than in its botany, they were quite indifferent whether the plant chosen to illustrate some particular point was a lily, a rose, a narcissus or an anemone. The saying of Isaiah, 'the desert shall rejoice and blossom as the rose,' is the first to come to mind and illustrates the point very well. Students of the ancient writings now agree that the word translated as 'rose' might just as well have been rendered 'lily', and say it meant the Polyanthus Narcissus, *N. tazetta*. We think of this as one of the more ordinary of the spring flowers, but Homer paid tribute to it,—'The Narcissus wondrously glittering, a noble sight for all, whether immortal Gods or mortal men; from whose root an hundred heads spring forth, and at the fragrant odour thereof all the broad heaven above, and all the earth laughed, and the salt-wave of the Sea.'

Lilies are mentioned many times and obviously refer to several very different plants. Just as we speak of the water-lily, lily-of-the-valley and calla lily without giving a thought to their botanical relationships, so did the people of biblical times. In I Kings 7, we are told of the lilies and lily-work used in the decoration of the temple, carvings that are known to represent the common white water-lily, *Nymphaea alba*, of the British countryside, along with the Egyptian Lotus, *N. lotus*, and the lovely blue *N. coerulea*. The 'lilies by the rivers of waters', Ecclesiasticus 50: 8, appear to have been the Yellow Flag, *Iris pseudo-acorus*, one of the most decorative of British wildflowers and believed to have been the original fleur-de-lis of France. Many candidates have been put forward for the honour of being the 'lily of the field' of the New Testament but most authorities favour the ubiquitous *Anemone coronaria*.

The lilies of the Song of Solomon include a 'lily of the valleys' which is most certainly not the north European plant we know as such and was probably the graceful wild hyacinth of Palestine, *H. orientalis*, an elegant maiden very different from the fat stumpy matrons that inhabit our spring gardens. The 'lily among thorns' sounds exactly like a modern description of the Madonna Lily, *L. candidum*, when it was found recently growing wild amond the hills of Galilee. There has been some controversy about the 'lily dropping sweet-smelling myrrh' some authorities favouring either *Lilium martagon* or the red *L. chalcedonicum* but the Crown Imperial is a close favourite. It is a native of Persia, and no doubt it graced King Solomon's garden. Its strange, foxy smell is beloved of the east but is repugnant to western people.

The roses of the Bible also cover several different plants which do not belong to the rose family. The 'rose of Sharon' appears to be identical with Isaiah's rose of the desert while the 'rose by the brook of the fields' is undoubtedly the Oleander. The rose of Jericho is difficult to place, Dr Post thinks it may have been one of the wild roses that grow on the banks of the Jordan while others favour such different plants as the Oleander and the handsome red *Tulipa sharonensis*, still very plentiful in the grassy plain of Jericho.

The modern Rose of Jericho is a very different plant and a most interesting one. Also known as the Resurrection Plant, *Anastatica hierochuntica* is an insignificant annual rarely more than about six inches in height. When the dry weather comes it sheds its small white flowers, drops its leaves, and rolls itself up into a skeleton-like ball. The root dies and the plant becomes a vagrant with no visible means of support and, blowing about in the wind, can be recognized as the 'rolling thing before the whirlwind' of Isaiah 17: 13. When the rainy season arrives, or the rolling ball finds itself in a wet place, the branches absorb any moisture they can find and open up to scatter their seeds. The plants do not come to life again, of course, but they are capable of retaining their hygroscopic properties for several years.

There can be no better way of illustrating the loose way in which lilies and roses were spoken of in the days before we took the elements of botanical classification for granted, than to refer to the Tudor herbalist, John Gerard. He published his *Herball* in 1597 and it gives an excellent picture of the botanical knowledge of the sixteenth century, about the time the Bible was being translated into English. When discussing the Madonna Lily, which he calls the White Lilly of Constantinople, he says 'The Lilly is called in Latine Rosa Junonis, or Juno's Rose, because it is reported it came up of her milke that fell on the grounde'.

THE SPICES OF KING SOLOMON'S GARDEN

The gardens of many eastern lands have not altered very much since the days of King Solomon. Then, as now, the provision of shade and water, luscious fruits and aromatic herbs were matters of prime importance and little attention was paid to flowers. The exact location of this famous garden is unknown but there is every reason to believe that it was quite near the palace, as was the custom of the time. In a fertile valley a few miles from Jerusalem there are three large reservoirs known to this day as the Pools of Solomon and traditionally believed to have been constructed by him. 'I made me great works; I builded me houses; I planted me vineyards: I made me gardens and orchards, and I planted trees in them of all kind of fruits: I made me pools of water, to water therewith the wood that bringeth forth trees.'

In the Song of Solomon (4: 12-16, 6: 11) we get a very interesting account of the various gardens—

'A garden enclosed is my sister, my spouse; a spring shut up, a fountain sealed.
Thy plants are an orchard of pomegranates with pleasant fruits; camphire and spikenard:
Spikenard and camphire; calamus and cinnamon, with all trees of frankincense; myrrh and aloes with all the chief spices:
A fountain of gardens, a well of living waters, and streams from Lebanon.
Awake, O north wind: and come south; blow upon my garden that the spices thereof may flow out. Let my beloved come into his garden and eat his pleasant fruits.'

'I went down into the garden of nuts to see the fruits of the valley, and to see whether the vine flourished, and the pomegranates budded.'

'Let us get up early to the vineyards; let us see if the vine flourish, whether the tender grapes appear and the pomegranate bud forth: and there I will give thee my loves.
The mandrakes give a smell, and at our gates are all manner of pleasant fruits, new and old, which I have laid up for thee, O my beloved.'

From this we can see that he had several different types of gardens and grew lilies and other flowers, a very unusual thing in those days. The enclosed gardens were rectangular in shape, the high walls being masked on the inside by informal hedges, a convention that lasted into the mediaeval gardens of Europe. There are several references to this type of garden, vineyard or orchard boundary in the Bible, e.g. Isaiah 5: 5. 'I will tell you what I will do with my vineyard: I will take away the hedge thereof and it shall be eaten up; and break down the wall thereof, and it shall be trodden down.'

Besides the more usual vineyards, and olive orchards he had a garden of nuts containing walnuts, pistachio nuts and almonds, but the most interesting feature was the garden of spices. The spice trade brought many contacts with the lands lying to the east, especially Arabia and India, and many of his plants came from thence but we have no evidence that he knew anything of any land lying to the westwards of Egypt and it would appear that no purely European species could have reached Solomon's garden. He evidently knew and loved his plants and liked to take people round the gardens and point out his rarities. Josephus, the Jewish historian *c.* A.D. 37-95, says Solomon 'was not unacquainted with any of the natures of his plants, nor did he omit to make enquiries about them, but described them all like a philosopher, and demonstrated his excellent knowledge of their several properties.' This statement is confirmed in the First Book of Kings where we are told he 'spake of the cedar that is in Lebanon, even unto the hyssop that springeth out of the wall.'

Camphire and saffron were local plants but most of the other spice plants came from far beyond the confines of his own realm. 'All trees of frankincense' seems to infer that there were more than just the common species from the other side of the Red Sea while Aloes indicates a tree from India. The fragrant gum of Sweet Aloes came from the Eaglewood, *Aquilarum agallochium*, and had long been used in embalming the dead.

Spikenard was made from the fragrant young shoots of a pink-flowered herb, *Nardostachys jatamansi*, whose home is in the western Himalayas. It was most jealously guarded for centuries and the commercial product, stems covered with the fibrous remains of the leaves looking like bundles of ermine tails, was something of a mystery. When dried they are made into an unguent whose aromatic perfume still finds a ready market in the east but is not at all attractive to western women. In biblical times it was made up in alabaster boxes and used for the ceremonial anointing of guests, and coming from such a long distance was very expensive, hence the significance of John 12: 3, 'then Mary took a pound of ointment of spikenard, very costly, and anointed the feet of Jesus, and wiped his feet with her hair: the house was filled with the odour of the ointment'.

Some would like to identify the calamus with the Sweet Flag, *Acorus calamus*, the scented reed that is so common in southern England, but the consensus of opinion favours the Ginger Grass, *Andropogon aromaticus*, from the western plains of India. Before the more potent Chinese Ginger had reached the western world it was a very valuable and important plant because its stems and leaves taste and smell strongly of ginger. Cattle are very fond of it, but unfortunately it taints their milk and their flesh and for this reason has fallen from its high estate to be regarded as something of a pest. It may be the 'sweet cane from a far country'. Jeremiah 6: 30.

Stacte, one of the ingredients of the holy incense, was made from the bark of *Styrax officinalis*, a lovely flowering shrub or small tree from the hills of Galilee, whose white flowers rival the orange-blossom in their beauty and fragrance. Camphire is another local plant, *Lawsonia inermis*, better known as the source of henna. From time immemorial the women of the East have gone out into the garden to gather its graceful panicles of fragrant blossom to be dried and hung in sachets around the neck. More important, however, are the small, oval leaves that when dried are made into the paste known as henna and ever popular for colouring the nails, soles of the feet and the hollows of the palms. Saffron crocuses probably grew by the side of a path because they had the reputation of flourishing under adversity. An old Greek gardener noticed that 'it loves to be trodden on, and grows the fairer when the root is crushed into the ground by the feet; wherefor it is fairer along roads and well-worn places'.

CEREALS, BITTER HERBS AND MANNA

Most of our commonest cereals such as wheat, barley and rye are known to have been used as food since the remotest times and they have always been supplemented by other small seeds such as Lentils, Cumin and Coriander. Lentils are the seeds of *Lens esculentum*, and it is interesting to know that a red-seeded variety is still being grown in Palestine that appears to be the same as the kind used to make the 'red pottage', so delicious 'that God Almighty might dip His finger in it', for which Esau sold his birthright, as described in Genesis 25: 29-34. It is usually grown in poor stony ground under the olive groves and all too often the yield gives but poor return for all the work involved.

Some of those small seeds were ground down to make a flour and others were used for flavouring, either as spices or condiments, or sprinkled on bread or cakes in much the same way as we still use carraway or poppy seeds. Chief among such must have been coriander, seeds of *Coriandrum sativum*, so well known to the writer of Exodus 16: 31 that, when describing manna he said, 'it was like coriander seed, white: and the taste was like wafers made with honey', taking it for granted that one would know what he meant. Other small seeds were the fitches and cumin mentioned in Isaiah 28: 27, 'the fitches are beaten out with a staff and the cumin with a rod'. Fitches were not vetches as some would have us believe but the black aromatic seeds of *Nigella sativa*, a neat little plant whose pale blue flowers are set among the fine foliage just like those of the better known annual 'Love-in-a-Mist'. Cumin, *Cuminum cyminum*, is a member of the Carrot family, whose seeds like those of carraway have long been used for flavouring. Theophrastus, writing about 300 B.C. mentions a curious superstition, 'There is one peculiarity told of this plant, they say that one must curse and abuse it while sowing it, if the crop is to be fair and abundant.'

The Common Flax, *Linum usitatissimum*, is usually accepted as one of the very oldest sources of fibre, linen cloth having been found around the earliest of Egyptian mummies. Long grown in Egypt, there is no doubt that it was well established in Palestine before the coming of the Jews, because in Joshua 2: 6, we are told how Rahab protected the Israelites spies and 'hid them with the stalks of flax which she had laid in order upon the roof'. The flax of Exodus 9: 31, 'and the flax and the barley were smitten', may refer to the linen flax but more probably meant the False Flax, *Camelina sativa*, also known as the 'Gold of Pleasure'. It is a pretty little yellow-flowered member of the Carrot family, somewhat similar to flax and grown for the sake of its edible seeds.

The first Feast of the Passover was a meal of 'unleavened bread, bitter herbs' as is explained in Numbers 9: 11, and undoubtedly those bitter herbs were some of the common salad plants we eat to-day. Endive, sorrel, chicory, and the young leaves of dandelions are usually accepted without any question and some authorities like to include mint, water-cress and even young mustard plants. The Egyptians were known to have eaten green herbs, mixed with either vinegar or some condiment and placed in a common dish where all could dip their morsels of bread during the meal.

In their 400 years of bondage the Jews, although slaves, appear to have had very much the same standard of living as the common people of Egypt, eating very much the same food. Then, as now, melons and cucumbers were very popular, either raw or cooked, and continued to be eaten after the wanderers settled down in the Promised Land. The lapful of wild gourds, gathered from a wild vine by one of the sons of the prophets during the time of scarcity at Gilgal, and 'shredded into the pot of pottage' thereby rendering it uneatable, as is recorded in II Kings 4: 39, 41 was undoubtedly the Bitter Cucumber, *Citrullus calocynthis*. A melon-like plant bearing beautifully mottled fruits, green and yellow, whose pulp is a drastic cathartic, nauseous and bitter to the taste, it has been identified as the Vine of Sodom, 'For their vine is the vine of Sodom and of the fields of Gomorrah', Deut. 32: 32. *Solanum incanum*, a silvery shrub with large prickly leaves and purple flowers is commonly known as the Apple of Sodom on account of its pretty orange-red berried fruits that ripen into hollow puff-balls which burst with a scatter of dust and seeds, fitting Josephus' apt description of 'Dead Sea fruits that tempt the eye, but turn to ashes on the lips'.

Jonah's gourd, that sprang up in a night to shelter him from the heat of the sun, Jonah 4: 6–9, has been the subject of considerable discussion and many plants from the common ivy to the castor-oil plant have been cast for the role. Canon Tristram, who investigated the subject on the spot, was unreservedly in favour of the quick-growing Abyssinian Gourd, *Lagenaria leucantha*, saying its claims are incontrovertible. 'It is used universally in the East on trellises for shading arbours,—and a most effective screen it is.'

Although they bemoaned their lot it is obvious that the Jews became used to many luxuries during their sojourn in Egypt and when they found themselves in the barren wilderness of Sinai bitterly did they reproach Moses for bringing them to 'this evil place'. They longed for the luscious fruits they had taken for granted, 'the figs, the pomegranates and the grapes', and detested the monotony of their present diet. Former hardships were forgotten and they longed for the 'cucumbers and melons, the leeks, the onions and the garlick; but now our soul is dried away and there is nothing at all, besides this manna, before our eyes.' Numbers 11: 6.

Manna is probably the most controversial of all the plant substances mentioned in the Bible, and many have been the attempts to explain what it could have been. 'And when the dew of the day was gone up, behold, upon the face of the wilderness there lay a small round thing, as small as hoar frost on the ground.' Exodus 16: 14. While some authorities have thought it may have been some sort of lichen, opinion has gradually crystallized around the exudations of two desert plants that are plentiful in the Sinai Peninsula, the Sinai Manna, *Alhagi maurorum*, and the Manna Tamarisk, *T. mannifera*.

The Sinai Manna is a spiny, scrubby bush belonging to the Pea family. In the heat of the day its leaves and prickly stems exude a sweet mucilaginous substance that hardens on exposure to the air. When hard the substance may be collected by spreading mats beneath the bushes. The Manna Tamarisk is a bigger plant, very similar to some of the Tamarisks commonly seen in our gardens. Burckhardt, the discoverer of Petra, who travelled through the Sinai wilderness in 1812, favoured the substance exuded by the Tamarisk and left a very interesting description of it. He thought it was caused by the

B

punctures of insects saying, 'In the month of June it drops from the thorns of the Tamarisk upon fallen twigs, leaves and thorns which always cover the ground beneath the tree in its natural state; the manna is collected before sunrise, when it is coagulated, but it is dissolved as soon as the sun shines upon it. The Arabs clear away the leaves, dirt, etc., which adhere to it, boil it, strain it through a piece of coarse cloth, and put into leathern skins; in this way they preserve it till the following year, and use it as they do honey, to pour over unleavened bread, or dip their bread into.

THORNS, BRIERS AND BRAMBLES

Spines and thorns are characteristic of the plants that grow under hard, arid conditions and there are very many of this type in modern Palestine, so many that it is somewhat difficult to decide which may have been the more prominent kinds in bygone ages. Three thousand years ago the land was well watered and wooded, the fields well cultivated and although the various thorny plants were always there in the background, waiting for a chance to invade the cultivated land, they were not so numerous as they are nowadays. Conditions do not seem to have altered very much during the past four centuries, however, because Newton, the English Traveller who visited the Holy Land in 1587, noticed, 'Thystles, briers and brambles, which grow out of the grounde themselves, without planting or husbandry, yielde in a manner no kind of commodity for the use of Man, but rather detriment and annoyance to Man by their prickles, and to the graine by their ill company and neighbourhood.'

In Proverbs 24: 30-31, we get an excellent account of what happened when the husbandman became lazy or inefficient, 'I went by the field of the slothful, and by the vineyard of the man void of understanding; and lo, it was all grown over with thorns, and nettles covered the face thereof.' Again and again we find the prophets of old using thorns, briers and brambles to give point to their prophecies of judgement and doom. 'And thorns shall come up in her palaces, nettles and brambles in the fortress thereof; and it shall be an habitation of dragons, and a court of owls.' Isaiah 34: 13.

The Nettles of these passages were undoubtedly the well-known Stinging Nettle, *Urtica dioica*, which together with three or four allied species is very common in Palestine, haunting the waste places just as happily as in other parts of the world. But the thorns and brambles might be almost anything, as Canon Tristram points out, there are upwards of twenty Hebrew words, used in the Authorized Version to indicate prickly plants, which have been indifferently translated as bramble, brier, thistle, or thorn and cannot easily be identified.

Most interesting of all thorns is that used for the crown of thorns and at least half a dozen common species have been put forward at one time or another as the plant in question. The Christ Thorn, *Paliurus spina-christi*, is a strong favourite on account of its thin flexible twigs that are fiercely armed with sharp spines, but Dr Post, who knew the flora of Palestine better than most people, would have none of it. He preferred the ubiquitous Spiny Burnet, *Poterium spinosum*, a tangled shrub bearing small reddish flowers and serrated leaves that disappear during the heat of summer, saying, 'Almost certainly the material used for Christ's crown of thorns. It is so abundant as to form in many places a prominent characteristic of the landscape.' He goes on to point out that it is 'extensively used for fuel for lime-kilns and for ovens.' When used for fuel in this way the branches are gathered and then cut up with pruning hooks and it is the only thorny plant to be used in this way. For this reason it is most suitable for identification with the 'thorns cut up', of Isaiah 33: 12, while the noisy way in which it burns, crackling and spitting, has led to the belief that it is the plant referred to in Ecclesiastes 7: 6, 'As the crackling of thorns under a pot, so is the laughter of a fool.'

TREES

In early times a fig tree, an olive and a grape vine and a well of sweet water were all that were necessary for a home and all through the Bible these three indispensables are referred to again and again as symbols of peace and plenty. In all there are some thirty different kinds of trees, the first being the gopher wood, the horizontal form of the Roman Cypress, *Cupressus sempervirens*, used by Noah in the construction of the ark, and the last the thyine wood of Revelations 18: 12. The latter is obtained from *Callitris quadrivalvis*, a cypress-like tree that grows wild in North Africa whose fragrant timber was the citrum wood of the Romans. The easily worked wood of the Sycomore, *Ficus sycomorus*, was a favourite building material until Solomon broke with tradition by selecting cedar of Lebanon for the temple. The 'cedar wood' used by the Jews during their sojourn in the wilderness of Sinai was not obtained from a true cedar but from several species of Juniper of which *J. phoenicia* is the most important.

The box referred to in Isaiah 60: 13, 'The glory of Lebanon shall come unto thee, the fir tree, the pine tree and the box together, to beautify my sanctuary', is essentially the same as the wild box trees that grow on Box Hill, in Surrey. This small tree is wide-spread over southern Europe to the hills of Persia and some authorities say the Palestine form should be called *Buxus longifolia*. The 'fir' has been identified as the Aleppo Pine, *Pinus halepensis*, and the 'pine' as the Stone Pine, *P. pinea*, whose edible seeds have long been popular as food. Husks of these large, nut-like seeds have been found in quantity in Roman refuse heaps in various parts of Britain, showing that they were sent to this out-post of the Empire as food for the soldiers.

The Nuts that Jacob sent to Egypt as part of the 'first fruits' were Pistachio nuts, seeds of *Pistacia vera*, which is closely related to the teil tree, the oak-like *Pistacia terebinthus* of Isaiah 6: 13. The story of Susannah and the Elders has been described as the first detective story, and gives a very good idea of a royal domain about 600 B.C. Daniel, as the clever young detective, confounds the nasty old men by pointing out that the tree under which they accused her of dallying could not have been both a Mastic tree, *Pistacia lentiscus*, and a Holm Oak, *Quercus ilex*, Susannah 54-58.

There are many references to oak trees and to the scarlet or crimson dye obtained from the kermes insect which infests the Kermes Oak, *Quercus coccifera*. 'And afterward came out his brother that had a crimson thread upon his hand', Genesis 38: 30. The Kermes Oak is smaller than, but easily confused with, Q. *pseudo-coccifera*, Abraham's Oak, so called because of the fine old specimen that lived at Mamre, at least until the turn of the century, and according to tradition marked the spot where the three angels were entertained unawares, as described in Genesis 18. Canon Tristram, who visited it about eighty years ago, says the trunk was 'about 22 feet in circumference, and quite sound, standing close to a vineyard in a grassy field, with some of its descendants not very far off and a well of sweet water nearby.'

No one has any doubt about the identity of the Shittim, or Setim, wood that was used for the tabernacle, 'And he made boards for the tabernacle of shittim wood', Exodus 36: 20, the usual explanation being that *Acacia seyal*, with its golden-haired tufts of blossom, is the largest tree growing in the wastes of Sinai. It is most unlikely that this was the main reason for its choice. As we have seen the Jews had absorbed many Egyptian customs and beliefs during their long sojourn in Egypt and it is now well known that the Egyptians had a tradition, already dating far back into the long-forgotten past, that the Acacia was a symbol of everlasting life. Even to-day Masons honour this old tradition by casting a sprig of Acacia into the open grave as part of their burial ceremony. There is a popular superstition that Acacia should never be cut or taken into the house because it is unlucky, a superstition that has spread to include the many different Australian Acacias that are comparative new-comers to our gardens. This is evidently a faint, far-off echo of the belief of the ancient Egyptians; it is easy to see how the emblem of immortality came to be associated with the burial service and that barbarians and unbelievers, ignorant of its inner significance, gradually came to think of it as a 'death token'. In course of time this would be toned down to a vague superstition that the 'Acacias are unlucky'.

About a dozen different willows grow wild in Palestine, including the White Willow, *Salix alba*, and the Crack Willow, *S. fragilis*, two widespread species that are equally plentiful in the British countryside. As might be expected those lush-growing trees did not pass unnoticed by the prophets of old. 'The shady trees cover him with their shadow, the willows of the brook compass him about', Job 40:22. The withs, as the flexible green twigs are sometimes called, have always been a handy and useful tying material. Samson said to Delilah 'If they bind me with seven green withs that were never dried, then I shall be weak, and as another man', Judges 16: 7. Green withs are still used in the same old way and there is a legend that one of the first, if not the first, specimen of the Weeping Willow to be grown in England was grown from a green with. About the middle of the eighteenth century Alexander Pope, the poet, saw Lady Suffolk undoing a packet of figs recently arrived from Smyrna and picking up the green with that bound it asked if he could have it saying, 'Perhaps this will produce something we have not in England.' In due course it grew to become one of the features of his garden by the side of the Thames, at Twickenham. The name Weeping Willow has become almost exclusively attached to the tree which Linnaeus named *Salix babylonica* under the impression that it was a native of the Near East, and the willow of Psalm 137:1–2, 'By the waters of Babylon there we sat down, yea, we wept when we remembered Zion. We hanged our harps upon the willows in the midst thereof.' The tree in question is *Populus euphratica* that, so far as I know is not yet in cultivation. The story of the Weeping Willow is old, very old, but it is not really a Bible plant. It is a native of China and the famous Willow Pattern gets its name from the gnarled old trees so familiar on the blue plates. No doubt it arrived as a green with in the Levant, probably after a long journey over the age-old caravan route through central Asia, but there is no evidence that it ever grew by the waters of Babylon.

The Judas Tree is so popularly associated with the Bible that, although it has no claim for inclusion, no account of Biblical plants seems to be complete without some mention of it. There is no record that Judas hanged himself on a tree and no reason to think that even if that did happen, he chose *Cercis siliquestrum*. So far as I have been able to find out the name was first used by Gerard in his *Herball* of 1597 and may have been founded on the old monkish legend that the flowers were originally white but, after the dreadful happenings that led up to the Crucifixion, the tree blushed with shame for the fruit it had to bear on that fatal day. It is a spectacular and distinctive flowering tree in the springtime when every twig is laden with reddish blossom and the reddish young leaves are budding. In France it is known as Arbre de Judea, the tree of the country, not the man, but the old story has gained such popularity that few trees are better known than the 'Judas tree, the tree on which Judas hanged himself'.

AARON'S ROD—THE ALMOND

AMYGDALUS COMMUNIS

GENESIS 43: 11

And their father Israel said unto them, If it must be so now, do this; take of the best fruits in the land in your vessels, and carry down the man a present, a little balm, and a little honey, spices, and myrrh, nuts and almonds.

EXODUS 37: 20

And in the candlestick were four bowls made like almonds, his knops and his flowers.

NUMBERS 17: 8

And it came to pass, that on the morrow Moses went into the tabernacle of witness; and behold, the rod of Aaron for the house of Levi was budded, and brought forth buds, and bloomed blossoms, and yielded almonds.

ECCLESIASTES 12: 5

Also when they shall be afraid of that which is high, and fears shall be in the way, and the almond tree shall flourish, and the grass-hopper shall be a burden, and desire shall fail; because man goeth to his long home, and the mourners go about the streets.

Plate 1. AARON'S ROD. *Amygdalus communis*

PLENCK: *Icones Plantarium Medicinalium. Vol. IV.*

AARON'S ROD—THE ALMOND

AMYGDALUS COMMUNIS

THE ALMOND TREE HAS BEEN VALUED FOR ITS FLOWERS AND FOR ITS SEEDS, WHICH produce a pleasant oil, since very early times, and the fact that Jacob thought almonds worth including in his present to an important Egyptian official shows that he thought of them as something of a luxury. The trees grow wild all over the Near East from the shores of the Mediterranean to the foothills of India, but many of them are thought to be descendants of cultivated plants whose original home is now unknown.

The Almond is the first of the flowering trees to bloom in Palestine, producing its lovely pink blossom from the bare and apparently lifeless branches, at a time when all the others are at rest. For this reason it came to be known as the Wake, or Wakeful, Tree, and the flowers were welcomed as the first sign of spring, a sign that 'winter is past, the rain is over and gone. The flowers appear upon the earth and the time of singing birds is come.' From this it was but a step to associate almond blossom with life after death, and to accept it as a symbol of the immortality of the soul, the resurrection of the spirit. With this background the blossoming of Aaron's rod takes on a new significance.

The cryptic passage in Ecclesiastes has had many interpretations and it may be that Dr Moffat's translation comes near the original message—'When old age fears a height and even a walk has its terrors, when the hair is almond-white and he drags his limbs along, and the spirit flags and fades.' The reference to almond-white hair may apply to the flowers, which are pink when seen close by but appear to be white when viewed from a distance. A grove of blossoming almond trees clothing a hillside has very much the effect of the silvery-white hair of old age.

Almonds do not grow in the wilderness of Sinai and the Israelites must have been impressed by the beauty of those that grew in Egypt when they used almonds as a pattern for their golden candlesticks. That happened a very long time ago, but such is the conservatism of craftsmen, the glass drops and rock crystal ornaments used in the decoration of candelabra are still known among glass-workers as 'almonds'.

APPLE—APRICOT

PRUNUS ARMENIACA

GENESIS 3: 6

And when the woman saw that the tree was good for food, and that it was pleasant to the eyes, and a tree to be desired to make one wise, she took of the fruit thereof, and did eat, and gave also unto her husband with her; and he did eat.

PROVERBS 25: 11

A word fitly spoken is like apples of gold in pictures of silver.

SONG OF SOLOMON 2: 3

As the apple tree among the trees of the wood, so is my beloved among the sons. I sat down under his shadow with great delight, and his fruit was sweet to my taste.

JOEL 1: 12

The vine is dried up, and the fig tree languisheth: the pomegranate tree, and the palm tree also, and the apple tree, even all the trees of the field are withered; because joy is withered away from the sons of men.

Plate 2. APRICOT. *Prunus armeniaca*

PLENCK: *Icones Plantarium Medicinalium. Vol. IV.*

APPLE—APRICOT
PRUNUS ARMENIACA

THE TALE OF EVE AND THE APPLE IS PROBABLY THE BEST KNOWN OF ALL THE BIBLE stories, and down through the centuries there has been a good deal of speculation as to which fruit it was that caused her downfall. Nowhere in the Scriptures are we told that the fruit was an apple and, nowadays, most of the authorities agree that whether or not it was a citron, a pomegranate, a quince or an apricot, it could not have been an apple.

The sweet, juicy apples that we take for granted are fruits that have all been developed within the past 150 years or so, mainly from a wild type known as the Paradise stock whose home is in the Caucasus Mountains. Dr Post, in his authoritative *Flora of Syria, Palestine and Sinai* says, 'Several poor varieties are in cultivation. The border of its native area touches ours, but I have not as yet seen any wild specimens.' It would appear that if apples were grown in Biblical times the fruit would have been small, acid and hard like the crabs still to be met with in old farm gardens. Such fruits would be quite unworthy of comparison with the grapes, figs and dates that grew in Solomon's garden.

Botanical classification was unknown before the seventeenth century and before that time almost any fruit was called an apple. Tomatoes were Love Apples and Dates were known as Finger Apples. In ancient times the citron was the Median or Persian Apple while the quince was the Cydonian Apple and the pomegranate the Apple of Carthage. Apricots were brought to England by Woolf, a gardener to Henry VIII and were known as Armenian Apples. William Turner, the Father of British Botany, writing about them in 1548 knew them under that name and gave 'Abrecok' as an English variant, saying, 'We haue very fewe of these trees as yet.'

Canon Tristram, who travelled widely in Palestine, is very much in favour of the apricot. 'For my part, I have no hesitation in expressing my conviction that the apricot alone is the apple of Scripture.' He points out in his *Land of Israel* how it meets all the requirements of the context.

'In highlands and lowlands alike, by the shores of the Mediterranean and on the banks of the Jordan, in the nooks of Judea, under the heights of Lebanon, in the recesses of Galilee, and in the glades of Gilead, the apricot flourishes, and yields crops of prodigious abundance. Its characteristics meet every condition of the "tappuach" of Scripture. "I sat down under his shadow with great delight, and his fruit was sweet to my taste." Near Damascus and on the banks of the Barada we pitched our tents under its shade, and spread our carpets secure from the rays of the sun. "The smell of thy nose (shall be) like 'tappuach'." There can scarcely be a more deliciously-perfumed fruit than the apricot; and what fruit can better fit the epithet of Solomon, "Apples of gold in pictures of silver", than this golden fruit, as its branches bend under the weight in their setting of bright yet pale foliage?'

BALM OF GILEAD (In early times)

BALANITES AEGYPTICA

GENESIS 37: 25

And they sat down to eat bread: and they lifted up their eyes and looked, and, behold a company of Ishmaelites came from Gilead with their camels bearing spicery, and balm and myrrh, going to carry it down to Egypt.

JEREMIAH 8: 22

Is there no balm in Gilead; is there no physician there? why then is not the health of the daughter of my people recovered.

JEREMIAH 46: 11

Go up into Gilead and take balm, O virgin, the daughter of Egypt: in vain shalt thou use many medicines; for thou shalt not be cured.

BALM OF GILEAD

COMMIPHORA OPOBALSAMUM

I KINGS 10: 10

And she gave the king an hundred and twenty talents of gold, and of spices a very great store, and precious stones: there came no more such abundance of spices as these which the Queen of Sheba gave to King Solomon.

EZEKIEL 27: 17

Judah, and the land of Israel, they were thy merchants: they traded in thy market wheat of Minnith, and Pannag, and honey, and oil, and balm.

BALM OF GILEAD
BALANITES AEGYPTICA
COMMIPHORA OPOBALSAMUM

TWENTY OR THIRTY YEARS AGO *CEDRONELLA TRIPHYLLA*, A DAINTY LITTLE PURPLE-flowered shrub, whose pale green leaves emit a pleasant aromatic fragrance when gently rubbed, was very popular as the Balm of Gilead. I grew it for a number of years, but lost interest when I realized that it is a native of the Canary Islands and can have had nothing to do with Palestine in Biblical times.

There has been considerable discussion about the true identity of the plant that produced the Balm of Gilead and most authorities now agree that it was originally a local plant, but that later the balm was imported from southern Arabia. Balm is first mentioned in the story of Joseph, son of Jacob, whose brethren were about to do away with him when 'they lifted up their eyes and looked, and behold, a company of Ishmaelites came from Gilead with their camels bearing spicery, and balm and myrrh, going to carry it down to Egypt.' Genesis 37: 25. With typical shrewdness the brethren saw a chance of making money, and sold their young brother into slavery.

That was not the last of him, however. Some twenty years later, about 1707 B.C., came a time of great scarcity throughout the Levant and Jacob sent the brethren into Egypt in search of corn. Joseph, who had by this time become a power in the land, recognized them and returned the purchase money hidden in the corn. They could not understand how it came to be there and, when a second expedition became necessary, had the gravest doubts as to their reception when they returned to Egypt. Jacob decided to send Pharaoh's steward a gift, saying, 'Take of the best fruits of the land in your vessels, and carry down the man a present, a little balm, and a little honey, spices and myrrh, nuts and almonds.' Genesis 43: 11.

The context of these two passages seems to demand a local product and the only plant capable of producing a gum that could be compared with the substance that has been variously known as Balm of Mecca, Balm of Jericho and Balm of Gilead, is *Balanites aegyptica*, a small scrubby tree that still flourishes among the limestone hills of Palestine. The Swedish botanist, Hasselquist, who was sent out to the Near East by Linnaeus to explore the plants of the region during the years 1749-52, had no doubt that Balanites supplied the Balm of Gilead. He described the substance as 'of a yellow colour, and pellucid. It is very tenacious or glutinous, sticking to the fingers, and may be drawn into long threads.' Strangely enough he goes on to confuse it with the Arabian balm, saying, 'I have seen it at a Turkish surgeon's, who had it immediately from Mecca, described it, and was informed of its virtues; which are first, that it is the best stomachic they know, and if taken to three grains strengthens a weak stomach; second, that it is a most excellent and capital remedy for curing wounds, for if a few drops are applied to fresh wounds, it cures it in a very short time.'

The Balm of Gilead of later times is derived from a tree that grows wild only in southern Arabia, but on account of the confusion that existed about the origin of the balm, it has been variously named *Amyris gileadensis*, *Balsomodendron gileadense* and *B. opobalsamum*, and is now *Commiphora opobalsamum*. Long known and valued in its homeland, the balm is said to have been introduced to the cities of the west when Balquis, Queen of Sheba, came to visit King Solomon about 995 B.C. When she came to see for herself the wonders of King Solomon's court and 'to prove him with hard questions', the queen 'came to Jerusalem with a very great train, with camels that bare spices.' Her present of spices was an eye-opener to King Solomon and led him to embark on the spice trade. She brought 'an hundred and twenty talents of gold, of spices a great store, and precious stones; and there came no more such an abundance of spices as these the Queen of Sheba gave to King Solomon.' I Kings 10.

It is said that he was so impressed by the virtues of the balm that he persuaded the queen to send him young trees or seeds and that these were planted in the Plain of Jericho where they came to be one of the treasures of the country. Be that as it may, there is no doubt that a grove or groves of balsam trees did flourish somewhere near Jericho for a very long time. We may never know whether or not they were planted there in the days of King Solomon, but they appear to have flourished until after the Moslems over-ran the country in the seventh century A.D.

It is interesting to hear what Theophrastus had to say about [illegible] C. He knew vaguely that they 'grow in a valley in Syria'. 'They [illegible] two parks in which it grows, one about four acres, the other [illegible] a good-sized pomegranate and is much branched [illegible] and it is evergreen; the fruit is like that of [illegible] is very fragrant, indeed, more so than [illegible]

'The gum, they say, is colle[illegible] piece of iron at the time of the Dog [illegible] are made both on the trunk and [illegible] all summer; but the quantity which [illegible] shell-ful; the fragrance is exceedi[illegible] small amount is perceived for a wide [illegible] known in Greece is very much adulte[illegible] From the larger park are obtained tw[illegible] pints, from the other only two such ves[illegible] silver; the mixed sort at a price proport[illegible] of exceptional fragrance.'

The balsam groves of Jericho were still f[illegible]es, and tradition, which loves to link its stories with the grea[illegible], having dealt with the Queen of Sheba, goes on to find a connection w[illegible]patra. The story goes that about 35 B.C. she wanted to visit Judaea and, having hea[illegible] that Herod was 'a bit of a lad among the ladies', wanted to visit him too. Anthony did not like the idea at all and somehow brought the conversation round to the balsam groves of Jericho, pointing out that they must be worth a pretty penny to Herod, at least 200 talents a year.—A talent may have been worth £250 of our money.—The upshot of it all was that Cleopatra came to own the groves and Herod had to pay her 250 talents a year for the privilege of extracting the gum. After that there was no more talk of visiting Jerusalem, no doubt Anthony dropped the hint that a grasping landlady is not a very romantic figure. Cleopatra seems to have insisted that a company of the Imperial Guard should be posted near the balsam groves to make sure that nothing should harm her valuable investment. The trees seem to have flourished until after the country was conquered by the Moslems in the seventh century. These people, coming from the east where the trees and their product were well known, appear to have thought nothing of the groves which had disappeared without a trace by the time the Crusaders reached the Holy Land in the eleventh century.

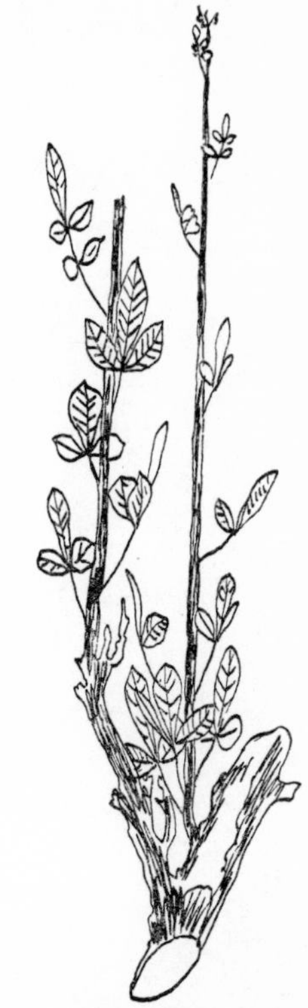

Although the balsams disappeared from Palestine a grove managed to survive in Egypt until about the seventeenth century. This grove grew at the Well of Matarya, not very far from Cairo and is said to have been planted in the days of Cleopatra, from seeds or young trees brought from Jericho. This well is famous for its old sycomore tree under which the Holy Family is said to have sheltered during the Flight into Egypt. It became a place of pilgrimage in the days of the early Christians and, at one time, there was a very interesting herb garden there. The balsams were of sufficient importance for that inveterate seeker of wonders, Sir John Maundeville, to think them worth a visit in 1322. He was not at all impressed and dismissed them as 'small trees that are no higher than the girdle of a man's breeches, and resemble the wood of the wild vine.'

The way in which Cedronella, Balanites and Commiphora have come to be entangled in the story of the Balm of Gilead is very typical of the confusion that surrounds the identity of many Bible plants.

COMMIPHORA OPOBALSAMUM

I have no idea of how or why Cedronella came to be accepted as the Balm of Gilead but there is no doubt that Balanites provided the balm of early times and was later superseded by the more potent balm from South Arabia. Balanites has come to be regarded as little more than an inferior interloper. Canon Tristram simply dismisses it as "a thorny tree with olive-like fruits from which the false Balm of Gilead, a sort of oil, is extracted and sold to pilgrims."

BAY TREE

LAURUS NOBILIS

PSALM 37: 35

I have seen the wicked in great power, spreading himself like a green bay tree.

Plate 3. BAY TREE. *Laurus nobilis*
Painted by PIERRE REDOUTÉ
DUHAMEL: *Arbres et Arbustes. Vol. II.*

BAY TREE
LAURUS NOBILIS

THE BAY TREE IS NOT NOW VERY COMMON IN PALESTINE, BUT IT IS STILL TO BE FOUND growing wild along the margins of brooks and streams and in moist valleys from the coast to the mountains. There, associated with the Myrtle and the Arbutus, it forms woods and thickets that are all that remain of the great forests that covered the land in bygone times. Where conditions are favourable the Bay is a tall tree, from 40 to 60 feet in height, whose handsome appearance is very striking in a land where so many of the trees are small, stumpy and thorny, twisted and weather beaten.

It may have been this air of evergreen luxuriance that caused the Psalmist to liken it to the 'wicked great in power'. In the imagery of the Bible it is easy to see an old Bay tree, towering 50 feet into the air and indifferent alike to winter storms and summer drought, troubles causing much distress to lesser beings, as a rich man happy in his prosperity and utterly indifferent to the poverty and want of the common people around him.

But it is on account of its association with the Greeks and Romans of classical times that the Bay tree is best known to us. Behind the rustle of its leaves are those fabled days when it was hailed throughout the known world as the symbol of triumph and distinction. It was awarded to the successful competitors in the Olympic Games and to heroes returning from the wars; laurel leaves were carried in triumph by generals on their way to report victorious campaigns in distant parts of the mighty Roman Empire; it was the laurel sacred to Apollo and used in several ways in his worship. The modern appellation Poet Laureate is a faint far-off echo of those distant days when people of distinction, especially poets and writers, were honoured by having their brows wreathed with chaplets of laurel and myrtle leaves as a tribute to genius.

One of the last heroes in Britain to be crowned with laurels was Sir William Wallace, the great Scottish Patriot, who led his countrymen against Edward I's attempt to usurp the Crown of Scotland at the end of the thirteenth century. Wallace, who was but the son of a private gentleman, was successful for a time, and being too modest to claim kingship styled himself Guardian of Scotland. Captured by his enemies he was brought to trial in Westminster Hall in 1306. When charged with treason he denied the charge, declaring with truth, that he could not be a traitor because he had never been a subject of the King of England, whereupon someone suggested that he be crowned with Elder leaves as a king of outlaws. This was doubly insulting because the Elder tree, with its rank, unpleasant smell and weak branches, was despised at that time as the tree on which Judas hanged himself. Edward, one of the wisest and bravest men of his time, would not allow this and ordered laurels to be used. This did not prevent the Patriot being condemned to death and executed with all the barbarism of the age.

‘BULRUSHES’—PAPER REED

CYPERUS PAPYRUS

EXODUS 2: 3

And when she could no longer hide him, she took for him an ark of bulrushes, and daubed it with slime and with pitch, and put the child therein; and she laid it in the flags by the river’s brink.

ISAIAH 18: 2

That sendeth ambassadors by sea, even in vessels of bulrushes upon the waters, saying, Go, ye swift messengers, to a nation scattered and peeled, to a people terrible from their beginning hitherto; a nation meted out and trodden down, whose land the rivers have spoiled.

ISAIAH 19: 7

The paper reeds by the brooks, by the mouth of the brooks, and everything sown by the brooks, shall wither, be driven away, and be no more.

'BULRUSHES'—PAPER REED

CYPERUS PAPYRUS

ONE OF THE BEST BELOVED OF THE BIBLE STORIES TELLS HOW PHARAOH'S DAUGHTER came to find the infant Moses in his ark of bulrushes and how she arranged for his own mother to come and nurse him. In those far-off times the most plentiful of all the reeds that grew along the banks of the Nile was the Paper Reed which, nowadays, is confined to the upper reaches and to Palestine.

A very elegant plant that grows only in shallow water, the Paper Reed sends its flexible green stems up to a height of ten to fifteen feet where they are surmounted by graceful tufts of light grassy foliage. It was from the pith of its stems, which may be up to three inches in diameter, that the first kind of paper was made. The pith was cut into thin strips and steeped in water, some think in ordinary Nile water while others believe that a small amount of gum was added, and laid in layers at right angles to each other. After being subjected to great pressure the material was dried and cut into suitable sizes, the best quality being polished with ivory.

Although we are indebted to the Paper Reed for bringing down some of the records from the long-forgotten past, its association with mankind goes much farther back into the beginnings of civilization. Without it Man might have had great difficulty in developing a settled existence in the tree-less valley of the Nile. The woody rootstock was valuable not only for burning but for making a variety of articles while the rind was woven into ropes, sails, mats and a kind of cloth. But above all the rootstock was a ready source of food. It could be roasted or eaten raw and was chewed for the sake of the sweet liquorice-like juice. More than 2,000 years ago Theophrastus noticed that 'they swallow the juice and spit the quid' and modern travellers have seen Ethiopians doing the same thing. Rafts of Papyrus stems, the vessels mentioned by Isaiah, are still in use in out of the way parts of the Near East.

Canon Tristram's description of the Marsh of Huleh serves to show what many quiet backwaters of the Nile, and many low-lying parts of Palestine must have looked like in Biblical times. 'The whole marsh is marked in the maps as impassable, and most truly it is so. I have never anywhere else met with a swamp so vast and so utterly impenetrable. First, there is an ordinary bog, which takes one up to the knees in water, then, after half a mile a belt of deeper swamp, where the yellow water-lily, *Nuphar lutea*, flourishes. Then a belt of tall reeds; the open water covered with white water-lily, *Nymphaea alba*, and beyond again an impenetrable wilderness of papyrus, *Cyperus papyrus*, in a beautiful forest of the richest green. It extends right across the east side, and so close are the arching stems that no bird can fly into it. A false step off its roots will take the intruder over head in suffocating deep mud.'

CEDAR OF LEBANON

CEDRUS LIBANI

II Kings 14: 9

And Jehoash the King of Israel sent to Amaziah, King of Judah, saying, The thistle that was in Lebanon sent to the cedar that was in Lebanon saying, Give thy daughter to my son to wife: and there passed by a wild beast that was in Lebanon, and trode down the thistle.

Psalms 29: 5

The voice of the Lord breaketh the cedars; yea, the Lord breaketh the cedars of Lebanon.

Ezekiel 27: 24

These were thy merchants in all sorts of things, in blue clothes and broidered work, and in chests of rich apparel, bound with cords and made of cedar, among thy merchandise.

CEDAR OF LEBANON

CEDRUS LIBANI

THE MIGHTY CEDAR FORESTS THAT COVERED THE HILLS OF LEBANON, THE 'TREES OF Jehovah, planted by his right hand, crowning the great mountains', were the epitome of majesty and power to the Jews. The proud Pharaohs of Egypt and the great kings of Assyria were compared with them and in those days both forest and empire must have seemed to be as permanent as the hills themselves. The forests were an unfailing source of timber and wealth that was eagerly exploited by all the ancient world, and now only a few scattered groves are left to tell of a glory that has gone. Solomon, who 'spake of trees from the cedar that is in Lebanon even unto the hyssop that springeth out of the wall' in one of the first botany lectures of which we have any record, was one of their most ruthless enemies.

He raised a levy of 30,000 Israelites and sent them in turns at the rate of 10,000 a month to cut down the trees, with the assistance of 150,000 slaves, and under the supervision of 3,300 officers. Seven years did they labour building a temple for the glory of God, and another thirteen building a private palace, the fabulous 'House of the Forest of Lebanon' that created such an impression on the Queen of Sheba.

This destruction would soon have been renewed had Nature been allowed to take her course, but Solomon had no idea of the damage he was doing and knew nothing of conservation. Goats were allowed to browse off the lush young growth that would soon have become forest again. Then wind and rain eroded away the rich top soil and the land, 'the good land, the land of brooks and water of fountains and depths that spring out of the valleys and hills', was left to become one of the most impoverished in all the world.

Fortunately a few scattered remnants of the forests managed to survive, mainly through the protection of the Patriarch of the Maronites, a Christian sect living on the slopes of Mount Lebanon, and it is still possible that in the future cedar forests may again clothe the hills of Lebanon.

CINNAMON AND CASSIA

CINNAMOMUM ZEYLANICUM AND C. CASSIA

EXODUS 30: 23

Take thou also unto thee principal spices, of pure myrrh five hundred shekels, and of sweet cinnamon half so much, even two hundred and fifty shekels, and of sweet calamus two hundred and fifty shekels.

PROVERBS 7: 17

I have perfumed my bed with myrrh, aloes and cinnamon.

SONG OF SOLOMON 4: 14

Spikenard and saffron; calamus and cinnamon, with all trees of frankincense; myrrh and aloes with all the chief spices.

CINNAMOMUM ZEYLANICUM

CINNAMON AND CASSIA

CINNAMOMUM ZEYLANICUM AND C. CASSIA

FEW OF OUR COMMON FOODSTUFFS HAVE SUCH A ROMANTIC STORY AS CINNAMON whose fame as a spice goes far back into remote antiquity. Cassia may be just as old but it has always been regarded as inferior to cinnamon by reason of its coarse and more pungent flavour. The best modern cinnamon comes from Ceylon and the best cassia from Cochin-China, but the trees from which they are derived grow all along the shores of southern Asia from the Malabar Coast and Ceylon, round the Malay peninsula to south China. The cinnamon and cassia of biblical times are believed to have come from the Malabar coast, but if silk could reach Palestine in the days of Ezekiel, about 600 B.C., there seems to be no reason why such easily transportable substances as these spices should not have come from much farther east.

We think of cinnamon as a substance whose primary use is to flavour food but in Biblical times spices were used in the preparation of incense and the holy oils used in religious rites, in medicine and as perfumes. In Proverbs 7: 17 the woman subtil of heart ensnared the young man devoid of understanding by decorating her room with tapestry and carved works, and fine linen from Egypt, and perfumed it with myrrh, aloes and cinnamon. In Roman times cinnamon was still used as a perfume; Martial satirises a dandy named Cotilus because he curled his hair and scented himself with cinnamon.

In Exodus 30: 23-5 directions are given for the preparation of the holy anointing oil, —'Take thou also unto thee principal spices, of pure myrrh five hundred shekels, and of sweet cinnamon half so much, even two hundred and fifty shekels, and of sweet calamus two hundred and fifty shekels, and of cassia five hundred shekels, after the shekel of the sanctuary, and of olive oil an hin: and thou shalt make it an oil of holy ointment, an ointment compound after the art of the apothecary: it shall be an holy anointing oil.'

This dates back to 1490 B.C. and seems to indicate that the Jews derived much of their knowledge of spices and their uses from the Egyptians who had been using such materials in religious rites and for embalming the dead for many centuries. About 2,500 B.C. a Pharaoh named Sankhkere sent ships down the Red Sea, and they are believed to have gone at least so far as the Gulf of Aden, to bring back spices. That was about 1,000 years before the famous expedition sent to the Land of Punt by Queen Hatshepset for incense and spice trees for the temple at Karnak. Modern gardeners know that cinnamon trees are very difficult to transplant from the open ground and that seeds will not grow unless planted as soon as they ripen. It seems very remarkable that Pharaoh's gardeners knew this nearly 4,500 years ago.

For hundreds of years the Arabs were the traders of the western world bringing their domestic and imported spices, gold, black slaves and other merchandise along the old caravan routes from south Arabia to Damascus and other cities around the eastern end of the Mediterranean. But centuries before that they had explored the seaways to the east and brought back riches, especially spices, to the Egyptians, Jews and Phoenicians. The most mysterious of all their spices were cinnamon and cassia. Both are the soft, inner bark of the young branches of trees, carefully removed and cut into strips about nine inches long and dried in the sun. In the process they roll themselves into quills that are collected into bundles each weighing about a pound. The reason for their peculiar shape, the methods of harvesting and the land of their origin were closely kept secrets for well-nigh 4,000 years, the best kept trade secrets of all time.

Although both these spices evidently came through a long line of coastal traders before they reached southern Arabia, the Arabs pretended that they came from the mountainous country along their own southern coast, or from Ethiopia, and had many stories to tell accounting for their scarcity and high price. Herodotus, the Greek historian who lived in the fifth century B.C., believed that Arabia was the only country producing cinnamon and cassia and explained how the Arabs collect them.

'Their manner of collecting the cassia is the following: They cover all their body and their face with the hides of oxen and other skins, leaving only holes for the eyes, and thus protected go in search of the cassia, which grows in a lake of no great depth. All round the shores and in the lake itself there dwell a number of winged animals, much resembling bats, which screech horribly and are very valiant. These creatures they must keep from their eyes all the while they gather the cassia.

'Still more wonderful is the mode in which they collect the cinnamon. Where the wood grows, and what country produces it they cannot tell—only some, following probability, relate that it comes from the country in which Bacchus was brought up. (Elsewhere he says that Bacchus was 'carried off to Nyssa, above Egypt in Ethiopia.') 'Great birds, they say, bring the sticks which we Greeks, taking the word from the Phoenicians, call cinnamon, and carry them up into the air to make their nests. These are fastened with a sort of mud to a sheer face of rock, where no foot of man is able to climb. So the Arabians, to get the cinnamon, use the following artifice. They cut all the oxen and asses and beasts of burthen that die in their land into large pieces, which they carry with them into those regions, and place near the nests; then they withdraw to a distance, and the old birds, swooping down, seize the pieces of meat and fly with them up to their nests; which not being able to support the weight, break off and fall to the ground. Hereupon the Arabians return and collect the cinnamon, which is afterwards carried from Arabia into other countries.'

A century and a half later Theophrastus noted that plants used for aromatic odours 'are found in the Arabian peninsula' but he thought others came 'partly from India whence they are sent over the sea, and partly from Arabia.' He, too, heard strange tales but he did not believe all of them. In the preparation of cassia he says, 'When they cut off the branches, they chop them up into lengths of about two fingers breadth or rather more, and these they sew up in a raw hide; and then from the leather and the decaying wood little worms are engendered, which devour the wood but do not touch the bark, because it is bitter and has a pungent odour.'

Cinnamon, 'they say grows in deep glens and that in these glens there are numerous snakes which have a deadly bite; against these they protect their hands and feet before they go down into the glens, and then, when they have brought up the cinnamon, they divide it up into three parts, and draw lots for it with the sun; and whatever portion falls to the lot of the sun they leave behind; and they say that, as soon as they leave the spot, they see this take fire. Now this is sheer fable.'

Pliny, who compiled his *Natural History* in the first century A.D., recapitulated the strange stories of the difficulties experienced by the Arabs in collecting cinnamon and cassia, saying, 'All these tales, however, have evidently been invented for the purpose of enhancing the prices of these commodities.' He is somewhat scornful of Herodotus and other ancient writers, being quite sure that 'Arabia produces neither cinnamon nor cassia, and this is styled "Happy" Arabia!' He goes on to say that both come from Ethiopia, being carried over vast tracts of ocean on a type of raft that is neither steered by rudder, nor propelled by oars or sails. 'Nor yet are they aided by any of the resources of art, man alone, and his daring boldness, standing in the place of all these.' He goes on to say that they choose the winter season, about the time of the equinox, for their voyage, and it is almost five years before the merchants effect their return, while many perish on the voyage.

This seems to indicate that some rumour of voyages to the far east had reached Pliny along with some faint echo of the monsoons driving the small ships along and making them fetch up against the Ethiopian coast. It may be that the Arab traders found some sort of aromatic bark in Ethiopia that could be used to adulterate the cinnamon and cassia, and it is known that these spices were adulterated with storax, laurel and other barks. Trans-shipment and adulteration may have taken place along the Ethiopian coast and the Arabians apparently led everyone to believe that their activities consisted of manufacturing the two spices from the products of that country.

DOVES' DUNG

ORNITHAGALUM UMBELLATUM

II Kings 6: 25

And there was a great famine in Samaria: and, behold, they beseiged it, until an ass's head was sold for four score pieces of silver, and the fourth part of a cab of doves' dung for five pieces of silver.

Plate 4. DOVES' DUNG. *Ornithagulum umbellatum*
Painted by PIERRE REDOUTÉ
REDOUTE: *Les Liliacees.*

DOVES' DUNG

ORNITHAGALUM UMBELLATUM

THIS LITTLE PLANT IS BETTER KNOWN IN OUR GARDENS AS THE STAR OF BETHLEHEM and there is some doubt as to whether or not it is actually mentioned in the Bible. Some writers have thought that doves' dung was really eaten, but there is ample evidence that the bulbs of this plant have long been regarded as suitable for food. They are said to be poisonous in the raw state, but quite pleasant to eat after having been boiled or roasted.

The Star of Bethlehem, along with several closely allied species, grows plentifully as a wildflower in the Holy Land and one traveller brought home a few bulbs collected from the temple area. It prefers stony hillsides and rocky places and paints them with the abundance of its blossoms until they have the appearance of cliffs and buildings whitened by the droppings of pigeons, hence the common name.

The botanical name *Ornithagalum*, literally birds' milk, obviously refers to this characteristic. Although it was adopted by Linnaeus two hundred years ago, under the impression that he was dealing with the doves' dung of Scripture, the name goes back to ancient times. Dioscorides, who is reputed to have been physician to Antony and Cleopatra, used it. He is known to have travelled widely over the Near East and he noted that the bulbs were eaten, 'dried, ground into powder, and mixed with flour'. Its reputation as a food plant travelled northwards with it. Parkinson, the last of the old English herbalists, knew it well and had a high opinion of it as being 'sweeter in taste to any chestnut and serving as well for a necessary need as for delight.'

Ever since the first inquisitive stranger carried off a few bulbs to grow in the garden at home, the Star of Bethlehem has gone on many journeys into many distant lands, and, having outstayed its welcome has colonized the waste places of the earth. As it became better known and loved its vague Biblical association as the Star of Bethlehem tended to be forgotten and other more friendly names arose. Because the pretty little green-backed stars come out only during the warmer parts of the day they have been called Sleepy Dick or Eleven o'clock Lady. As children we used to call them the Fairy Flowers because of the mysterious way in which they could vanish away in the long grass at the first touch of a chilly wind.

FIG

FICUS CARICA

JUDGES 9: 10-11

And the trees said to the fig tree, Come thou and reign over us.
But the fig tree said unto them, Should I forsake my sweetness, and my good fruit, and go to be promoted over the trees?

II KINGS 20: 7

And Isaiah said, Take a lump of figs. And they took and laid it on the boil and he recovered.

REVELATIONS 6: 13

And the stars of heaven fell unto the earth, even as a fig tree casteth her untimely figs, when she is shaken of a mighty wind.

FIG
FICUS CARICA

NOW WIDESPREAD OVER THE WARM TEMPERATE PARTS OF THE WORLD, THE FIG TREE grows wild in south-western Asia and is believed to have been first domesticated in south Arabia. Figs have been a very important article of food in that region since the very dawn of civilisation and the plants, sometimes no more than great sprawling shrubs, become trees some 30 feet in height when conditions are to their liking. Such trees are both common and conspicuous in Palestine, in gardens, overshadowing wells, and marking the boundaries of farms or small pieces of cultivated land.

There are more than forty references to figs in the Bible and their importance in the lives of the people is nowhere better shewn than in I Kings 4: 25 when discussing the peace and prosperity enjoyed under Solomon, 'And Judah and Israel dwelt safely, every man under his vine and under his fig tree, from Dan even to Beer-sheba, all the days of Solomon.'

Six varieties of fig were grown in Italy at the beginning of the Christian era and probably some of the hardiest of them were grown in Britain by Roman and Romanized British gardeners, but there is no evidence that any fig trees survived the troubled centuries between the fall of Rome and the first of the monastery gardens. Several monkish traditions tell of the introduction of fig trees in later times. Thomas à Becket, returning from a pilgrimage to Rome is credited with having brought home the first fig tree and planted it at Tarring in Sussex. Another older tradition says that, long before his time, in the days of the Norman kings, Abbé de Fécamp planted the first fig tree to grow in English soil at the nearby Sompting Abbots, thereby starting off the cultivation of figs in England.

The oldest fig trees in England, however, are probably those planted in the Lambeth Palace garden by Cardinal Pole during his Primacy, 1554-1558. They were severely damaged during the severe winter of 1813-14 and had to be cut almost to ground level, but they survived and flourished. Miss Gladys Taylor, in her most interesting 'Old London Gardens'* says, 'To-day (1953) they form a thick shrubby screen outside the south wall of the old library. In fact, the trees are emulating the banyan in that many branches are layering themselves. To step behind that barrier of fig leaves is to find oneself in a green, twilit jungle of twisting branches and dense foliage. There are about five trees and all but one are the White Marseilles variety that ripen in profusion and can be preserved as well as eaten raw. The exception is a Black Turkey fig that does not attain perfection in this country."

These trees are flourishing after 400 years so it is not impossible for a few fig trees in sheltered corners to have lived in southern England from the fall of Rome until the eighth or ninth centuries when the first monastery gardens began to appear.

* *Published by Batsford.*

FRANKINCENSE

BOSWELLIA CARTERI

LEVITICUS 5: 11

But if he be not able to bring two turtle doves, or two young pigeons, then he that sinned shall bring for his offering the tenth part of an ephah of fine flour for a sin offering: he shall put no oil upon it, neither shall he put any frankincense thereon: for it is a sin offering.

I CHRONICLES 9: 29

Some of them also were appointed to oversee the vessels and all the instruments of the sanctuary, and the fine flour, and the wine, and the oil, and the frankincense, and the spices.

JEREMIAH 6: 20

To what purpose cometh there to me incense from Sheba, and sweet cane from a far country?

MATTHEW 2: 11

And when they came into the house, they saw the young child with Mary his mother, and fell down and worshipped him: and when they had opened their treasures, they presented unto him gifts; gold, and frankincense and myrrh.

MYRRH

COMMIPHORA MYRRHA

EXODUS 30: 23

Take thou also unto thee principal spices, of pure myrrh five hundred shekels, and of sweet cinnamon half so much, even two hundred and fifty shekels, and of sweet calamus even two hundred and fifty shekels.

MARK 15: 23

And they gave him to drink wine mingled with myrrh; but he received it not.

JOHN 19: 39

And there came Nicodemus, which at first came to Jesus by night, and brought a mixture of myrrh and aloes, about an hundred pound weight.

FRANKINCENSE AND MYRRH

BOSWELLIA CARTERI. COMMIPHORA MYRRHA

GOLD, FRANKINCENSE AND MYRRH! THESE WERE THE TREASURES THE THREE WISE MEN from the east brought as gifts to the Infant Jesus, and their choice shows clearly that the spices were second only to the gold in value. We find it difficult to appreciate the importance of spices and perfumery in the ancient world, probably because we fail to realize how strong were the smells and the vast quantities of fragrant herbs and spices needed to drown unpleasant odours and keep the flies at bay.

Since far, far away down the dark corridors of time mankind has thought of foul and unpleasant smells as manifestations of evil, manifestations that could only be overcome by the pleasant fragrance of healing herbs and simples. Thus it happened that such fragrant substances came to play a very important role, not only in religious rites, but in the everyday life of the people. Needless to say, the discovery that these self-same substances could be employed to prevent the corruption of the body after death did much to enhance their prestige.

For countless centuries south Arabia was the spice emporium of the ancient world. It is the home of the most precious of spices, frankincense, myrrh and balm of Gilead, all of which are fragrant gum-resins extracted in much the same way from wild trees. When the Queen of Sheba came to visit King Solomon the Jews were astonished by the quantity of spices she brought and about 1,000 years later her people were still the leading spice traders of the world. Strabo, the Greek writer who lived at the time of Christ, recorded that the Sabaeans, the people of Sheba, had become the richest of all the Arab tribes through their trade in spices. They are said to have lived in luxury in magnificent houses whose doors and walls were inlaid with silver and gold, and so rich was the community that 'even a camel driver might attain some sort of riches'. But, he pointed out, 'the part of Arabia that produces spices is small, and it is from this small territory that the country got the name "blest", because such merchandise is rare in our part of the world and very costly.'

This profitable trade, carried over the ancient caravan routes to Petra, Palmyra and Damascus lasted until the Portuguese found their way round the Cape of Good Hope at the end of the fifteenth century. Its most valuable elements were frankincense and myrrh, but cinnamon and other spices from farther east, along with the ivory, apes and black slaves of East Africa were all important. The caravans were a source of riches to all who lived along the route, for they had to pay heavy tolls and dues at every stopping place. They dare not go off the beaten track on pain of death and the only return for these continuous levies were shelter at night and perfunctory protection from robbers.

Vast quantities of frankincense and myrrh along with other spices were in constant demand for religious ceremonies, and for embalming the dead, all over the Near East. We are told that when Poppaea, the wife of Nero, died her body was embalmed after the manner of eastern queens and that Nero used up more than a year's supply of myrrh, frankincense and cinnamon in the funeral rites. At the Feast of Isis, for example, the Egyptians made a burnt offering of an ox whose carcase was filled with frankincense and myrrh so that the aromatic fumes of the spices should mask the smell of burning flesh. There are many references to the use of frankincense and myrrh in the Old Testament.

The true Myrrh is a clear oily resin secreted by *Commiphora myrrha*, and a few other closely related species that are still plentiful among the hills of Abyssinia, Somaliland and Arabia. It is soft and rather sticky at first but soon hardens to become a white or yellowish-brown gum that still has its place in modern commerce.

Frankincense, the true incense, so called because it is so much superior to many other substances at one time sold as incense, is obtained from several species of trees that were named *Boswellia* in the eighteenth century, in honour of James Boswell, Dr Johnson's friend and biographer. The frankincense of early times came from *B. carteri* which flourishes in the arid, semi-desert country on both sides of the Red Sea, but as trade developed a higher grade came to be imported from Malaya and the East Indies. The shores of East Africa are believed to be the Land of Punt to which Queen Hatshepset of Egypt sent her five ships in 1570 B.C. in search of spices. The record of this successful expedition may still be read on the walls of a temple at Karnak. It tells of the heaps of myrrh-resin, cinnamon wood and eye-cosmetic brought back from that fabled land, and also of the live incense and myrrh trees planted in the temple garden.

Theophrastus gives an interesting account of the frankincense and myrrh trees. 'The trees of frankincense and myrrh grow partly in the mountains and partly on private estates at the foot of the mountains. The mountains, they say, are lofty and forest-covered, and subject to snow, and rivers flow down to the plain. The frankincense tree, they say, is not tall, about five cubits high, and is much branched; it has a leaf like that of a pear, but much smaller and very grassy in colour, like rue, the bark is altogether smooth, like that of bay.

'The myrrh tree is said to be still smaller in stature and more bushy, is spinous, with a leaf like that of an elm except that it is curly, and spinous at the tip, like that of a kermes oak.'

Times have changed, but the old customs linger on in remote places. Doughty, in his *Travels in Arabia Deserta*, written some 80 years ago, said 'Frankincense is no more of Arabia Felix, and yet the perfume is sovereign in the estimation of all Arabians. The most is brought now in pilgrimage from the Malay Islands to Mecca; and from thence is dispersed throughout the Arabian peninsula, almost to every household. The odour comforts the religious soul and embalms the brain: that we think the incense-odour religious, is by great likelihood the gentile tradition remaining to us of this old gold and frankincense road. The Arabians cast a morsel in a chafing dish, which is sent round from hand to hand in their coffee drinkings, especially in oases villages in any festive days: each person, as it comes to him in turn, hides this under his mantle a moment, to make his clothing well smelling; then he snuffs the sweet reek once or twice, and hands down the perfume dish to his neighbour.' This old custom may be referred to in Psalm 45: 18, 'And all thy garments smell of myrrh, and aloes and cassia.'

Myrrh is the first and last substance to be associated with the life of Christ. When the three wise men from the east came to adore him they 'opened their treasures, they presented unto him gifts; gold frankincense and myrrh.' Matthew 2: 11. Mark says that at the time of the Crucifixion the Roman soldiers offered him a drink of wine mingled with myrrh, but the other Apostles, when describing the same incident tell us that it was vinegar, or vinegar mixed with gall, so that all we can be sure of is that it was some sort of bitter, probably narcotic drink. When Joseph of Arimathaea and his friends came to claim the body after the Crucifixion they decided to embalm it. Nicodemus, who must have been a rich man, 'came to Jesus by night, and brought a mixture of myrrh and aloes, about an hundred pound weight. Then took they the body of Jesus, and wound it in linen clothes with the spices, as the manner of the Jews is to bury.' John 19: 39-40.

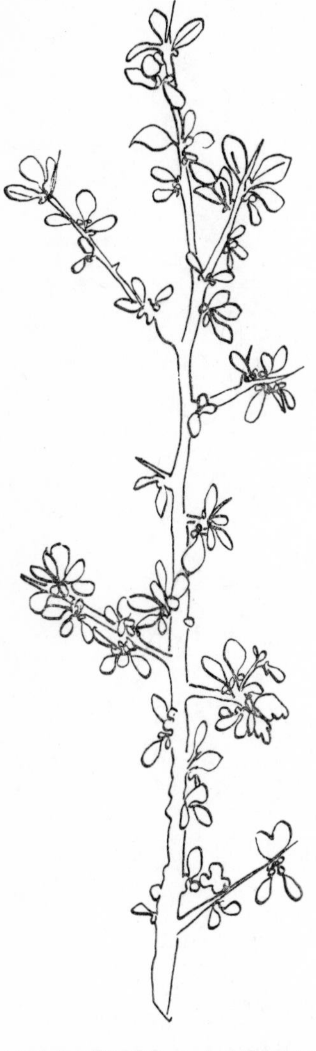

COMMIPHORA MYRRHA

BOSWELLIA CARTERI

LILY AMONG THORNS

THE WHITE LILY

LILIUM CANDIDUM

Song of Solomon 2: 2

As the lily among thorns, so is my love among the daughters.

Plate 5, LILY. *Lilium candidum*

Painted by PIERRE REDOUTÉ

REICHENBACH: *Icones Florae Germanicae. Vol. II.*

LILY AMONG THORNS

LILIUM CANDIDUM

'THREE BRILLIANTLY WHITE BLOOMS OF THIS MAJESTIC FOREST PLANT, ON A 121 CM. long stem, shone forth among limestone rocks and the shrubs of moderately dense maqui.' With those words Mr H. Boyko tells how he found the White Lily growing wild on Mount Carmel in May 1945, and the picture he gives is very similar to the Bible passage.

The White or Madonna Lily has been found doubtfully wild all over the Mediterranean basin from France to the hills of Syria, an area that was well within the confines of the Roman Empire. The suggestion has been made that, because few of these colonies seem to be capable of setting seeds they must have been planted, and, because in olden times they were of some medicinal importance, that they were planted near Roman outposts as a handy source of *materia medica.*

Until the present century no one seems to have come across colonies of White Lilies that were indubitably wild, but in 1916 some were found growing through prickly bushes about 30 miles from Salonika. When brought into cultivation they were found to seed freely. About the same time another colony was discovered high up among bush-clad cliffs in Macedonia and a few years later more were found. This colony was discovered at an altitude of 4,000 feet on the rocky limestone cliffs of a valley near the Albanian border. In each case those who found the plants were convinced that they were truly wild.

They had long been known from Lebanon but no one had found any colonies of the White Lily in Palestine until 1925 when M. N. Naftolsky, a well-known plant-hunter, who was leading a party of students from the Hebrew University in Jerusalem, came across some plants in the mountains of upper Galilee. We can no longer doubt that in Biblical times the White Lily was plentiful in Palestine, but with the decimation of the forests, and the drying up of creeks and streams, the plants were unable to adapt themselves to the changed conditions and gradually disappeared. Disappeared except for a few scattered remnants that have taken refuge in moist places inaccessible to stock. They are enough, however, to show that at one time the White Lily may have been widespread in Biblical lands, making it a strong candidate for the 'lily among thorns'.

LILY OF THE FIELD

ANEMONE CORONARIA

MATTHEW 6: 28, 29

And why take thought for raiment? Consider the lilies of the field, how they grow: they toil not, neither do they spin:
And yet I say unto you, That even Solomon in all his glory was not arrayed like one of these.

LUKE 12: 27

Consider the lilies how they grow: they toil not, they spin not; and yet I say unto you, that Solomon in all his glory was not arrayed like one of these.

LILY OF THE FIELD
ANEMONE CORONARIA

THERE HAS BEEN MUCH ARGUMENT OVER THE TRUE IDENTITY OF THE VARIOUS 'LILIES' referred to in the Bible. It should be remembered that in those days botanical classifications were unknown and plants were known by their 'common names' only. We, ourselves, speak of the primrose and the lily-of-the-valley knowing full well that the plants do not belong to the rose or the lily families. Thus we can see that the various plants called 'lilies' in the Bible need not necessarily have been true lilies, nor the same plants on each occasion.

Many and various are the Palestinian wildflowers that have been suggested as the lily of the fields. Some writers think they may have been drifts of White Lilies, *Lilium candidum*, swaying in the breeze, while others favour the crimson *Tulipa sharonensis* common in sandy places in the coastal plain, or one of the Gladioli such as the common pink *G. segetum* of the grainfields, or *G. aleppicus*, 'the purple lily that o'ertops the corn'.

But the wildflower that catches the eye of the traveller in the springtime, the flower that paints the whole countryside with great splashes of purple scarlet, reminiscent of the barbaric splendour of an eastern monarch is *Anemone coronaria*. Canon Tristram sums up the position: 'there have been many claimants for the distinctive honour of "the lilies of the field"; but while it seems most natural to view the term as a generic expression, yet if one special flower was more likely than any other to catch the eye of the Lord as He spoke, no one familiar with the flora of Palestine in springtime can hesitate in assigning the place to the anemone.'

Anemones, the Daughters of the Wind, which according to Pliny only opened their flowers when the wind was blowing, were great favourites in classical times for making the chaplets and garlands that formed an essential part of all public rejoicing. This one was known as the 'Blood of Adonis', the explanation being that when Adonis was killed by a wild boar Venus caused the flowers to spring up where his blood had soaked into the ground. Christianity, which absorbed as many as possible of the old customs and beliefs had no trouble with this one, the flowers simply became 'Blood Drops of Christ'.

The year 1596 is usually given as the date of its introduction into English gardens but it seems unlikely that such colourful flowers, that are so easily transported, should not have arrived and been lost long before. It seems very unlikely that it was overlooked by returning Crusaders or wandering friars. By the middle of the seventeenth century thirty different varieties were being grown in England, and the Anemones appear to have been even more popular on the Continent.

A certain Maître Bachelieu is said to have grown a particularly good strain in his Paris garden. He would not part with either roots or seeds and the Burgomaster of

[*continued at foot of page* 48

LOCUSTS—HUSKS

CERATONIA SILIQUA

MATTHEW 3: 4

And the same John had his raiment of camel's hair, and a leathern girdle about his loins; and his meat was locusts and wild honey.

LUKE 15: 16

And he would fain have filled his belly with the husks that the swine did eat; and no man gave unto him.

Antwerp, after trying to get some by every legitimate means for about ten years, resorted to low cunning. He, accompanied by a servant, went to see Maître Bachelieu at a time when he knew the fluffy anemone seeds would be ripe. As usual he was shown round the garden and, unfortunately, just as he was passing the Anemone bed, his fur cloak slipped off his arm. The servant darted forward and took the cloak to the awaiting carriage before Maître Bachelieu realized what had happened. The seeds were carefully preserved and sown and 'next year the Burgomaster shar'd the produce of his expedition with all his friends, and by their agency imparted it to all Europe'. For long afterwards the flowers were known as the 'French Anemones', a name that still lingers in North America.

Plate 6. LOCUST. *Ceratonia siliqua*

Painted by FRIEDRICH GUIMPEL

HAYNE: *Getreue Darstellung und Beschreibung in der Arzneykunde. Vol. VII.*

LOCUSTS : HUSKS
CERATONIA SILIQUA

ALTHOUGH BEST KNOWN AMONG ENGLISH-SPEAKING PEOPLE AS THE 'LOCUST' THIS plant has many names including Carob, Karoub, Algaroba and St John's Bread. Some commentators, being unwilling to believe that John the Baptist did eat locusts, have thought that the term 'locusts and wild honey' means the seeds and sweet pulp of the Carob Tree, but all are agreed that the husks eaten by the prodigal son were dry carob pods. Very palatable to man and beast and reputed to have been an article of food among the poor of the Near East, from time immemorial, the inferences are that they were not accepted as such in Jesus' day.

The Locust is a medium-sized tree with dark evergreen leaves and inconspicuous flowers which produce narrow pods some four inches long and about an inch wide. It does not appear to have been cultivated until historical times, being brought to southern Europe by the Greeks and Romans. It was spread over north Africa and reached Spain in the days of the Moors and Locust pods were the main sustenance of Wellington's cavalry during the Peninsular War. Up to the days of mechanisation they were the chief food of British army horses in Egypt and Malta. Good trees are said to yield up to 3,000 lbs. of pods per annum and these are still an important forage crop in the Mediterranean basin.

Everyone knows the story of Rip van Winkle without realizing that it is a modern version of an old Jewish legend. The Rabbi Chomi went for a stroll one evening and came across an old man planting a Locust seed. Laughingly he asked why an old man should take the trouble knowing that it would take 30 years to come to maturity, to be told by the planter that he had eaten many Locusts planted by other men and he would like to leave a tree for his children. Presently the Rabbi wearied and sat down to rest. When he woke the sun was rising and he hastened home thinking the family would be worried by his absence all night. Then he noticed a fine Locust tree growing where he had seen the old man planting his seed and when he reached the village found that all men were strangers. Gradually it was borne in upon him that he had slept for seventy years.

MULBERRY

MORUS NIGRA

I CHRONICLES 14: 15

And it shall be, when thou shalt hear a sound of going in the tops of the mulberry trees, that then thou shalt go out to battle: for God is gone forth before thee to smite the host of the Philistines.

EZEKIEL 16: 10

I clothed thee also with broidered work, and shod thee with badgers' skin, and I girded thee about with fine linen, and I covered thee with silk.

I MACCABEES 6: 34

And to the end they might provoke the elephants to fight, they showed them the blood of grapes and mulberries.

Plate 7. MULBERRY. *Morus nigra*
Painted by PIERRE REDOUTÉ
DUHAMEL: *Arbres et Arbustes. Vol. IV.*

MULBERRY

MORUS NIGRA

ALL WHO ARE FAMILIAR WITH MULBERRY TREES WILL AGREE THAT THEY HAVE SOFT leaves that do not make any noise when stirred by the breeze, quite unlike the hard, long-stalked leaves of the poplar. For this reason it seems much more likely that the noise in the tops of the trees was made by poplars and that mulberries had nothing to do with the rout of the Philistines.

The derivation of the ancient Latin name, *Morus*, is uncertain, but it may have come from mora—meaning late—because of the late appearance of the leaves in spring. The Ancients were very much impressed by this characteristic and dedicated the Mulberry to Minerva as 'the wisest of the trees' because it was content to wait until all danger of frost was over instead of rushing into growth at the first hint of fine weather.

Confusion between the Black Mulberry from western Asia and the White Mulberry of China caused many difficulties in the establishment of the silk industry in the western world. The Chinese tree is the natural host of the silk-worm and both have been found wild in the mountains of southern Mongolia. The creatures feed on leaves of the Black Mulberry but the results are not very satisfactory.

Silk has been known in China since about 4,000 B.C. but the first silk-worms did not reach Byzantium until the sixth century A.D., having been smuggled out of China by two Nestorian monks. Even so, the silk industry took nearly 1,000 years to become established in France where James I cast a jealous eye upon it and decided to foster silk-making in England. He set an example by enclosing four acres of waste land, near the site of the present Buckingham Palace, and planting it in Mulberry trees. This Mulberry Garden became a fashionable resort for a time but its popularity waned about 1670 and it was closed a few years later.

This attempt to establish silk-growing in England was not a success, partly on account of the climate, but mainly because Black Mulberry trees were distributed instead of the white kind. In the reign of Charles II John Evelyn pointed out that the White Mulberry was used in France and said he had some trees flourishing in his garden. He was too late, however. The Mulberry Garden was closed and King James' experiment had long been written off as both expensive and unsuccessful.

MUSTARD

BRASSICA NIGRA

MATTHEW 13: 31, 32

Another parable put he forth unto them, saying, The kingdom of heaven is like to a grain of mustard seed, which a man took and sowed in his field: Which indeed is the least of all seeds: but when it is grown, it is the greatest among herbs, and becometh a tree, so that the birds of the air come and lodge in the branches thereof.

MARK 4: 31, 32

It is like a grain of mustard seed, which, when it is sown in the earth, is less than all the seeds that be in the earth: But when it is sown, it groweth up, and becometh greater than all herbs, and shooteth out great branches; so that the fowls of the air may lodge under the shadow of it.

LUKE 13: 19

It is like a grain of mustard seed, which a man took, and cast into his garden; and it grew, and waxed a great tree; and the fowls of the air lodged in the branches of it.

Plate 8. MUSTARD. *Brassica nigra*
Painted by JOHANN BAYER
HORNEMANN: *Florae Danicae. Vol. IX.*

MUSTARD

BRASSICA NIGRA

MUSTARD IS BELIEVED TO HAVE ORIGINALLY BEEN A WEST ASIAN WILDFLOWER THAT invaded man's grainfields soon after he began cultivating them and, like the Corn Poppy and the Corn Marigold, has followed him around ever since. In course of time, however, its oil and the pungent flavour of its crushed seeds came to be appreciated and it became a crop in its own right. Mustard is still a common agricultural crop in the Near East, being grown not only for the oil but for fodder and for the mustard of commerce.

In northern Europe and other cool parts of the world it may be found as a wayside plant, a summer annual rarely more than about thirty inches in height. But in warmer climates it may be more than five times that size. One writer noted 'Mustard, which is systematically planted for fodder, grows with the greatest luxuriance in Palestine. The comparison between the size of the seed and the plants' great height was already proverbial when Jesus used it.'

There has been much argument as to whether or not it really was Mustard that grew 'from the least of all seeds' to become a 'great tree', but close acquaintance with mustard plants as they grow in Palestine leaves no doubt. The mustard seed that a man was likely to 'cast into his garden' was the smallest of the farm and garden seeds known to the simple people who listened to the parable. Of course mustard would not grow into 'a great tree'. We have been brought up to take the Bible so seriously and so very literally that we tend to forget that the gospels were written by people like ourselves who would use a telling phrase even if it were not strictly correct. Many travellers in Palestine, in Egypt, and in California have told of riding through thickets of wild mustard on horseback and of having been unable to see over the tops of the plants. It is on record that well irrigated crops may reach sixteen feet in height and one traveller in Egypt said he actually saw birds nesting among mustard plants.

MYRRH (LADANUM)

CISTUS SALVIFOLIUS or C. VILLOSUS

GENESIS 37: 25

And they sat down to eat bread: and they lifted up their eyes and looked, and, behold, a company of Ishmaelites came from Gilead with their camels bearing spicery, and balm and myrrh, going to carry it down to Egypt.

GENESIS 43: 11

And their father Israel said unto them, If it must be so now, do this: take of the best fruits in the land in your vessels, and carry down the man a present, a little balm, and a little honey, spices, and myrrh, nuts and almonds.

Plate. 9 MYRRH. *Cistus villosus*

Painted by J. HART

SWEET: *Cistineae of the Natural Order of Cistus.*

'MYRRH' OF THE EARLIEST TIMES—LADANUM

CISTUS SALVIFOLIUS or C. VILLOSUS

THE 'MYRRH' OF THE PASSAGES QUOTED MUST HAVE BEEN A LOCAL PRODUCT and for that reason cannot be the same as the 'Myrrh' referred to later in the Bible. The material is now known to have been ladanum, sometimes spelt labdanum or laudanum, a fragrant resinous substance obtained from the leaves and young growths of various species of *Cistus* that are commonly known as Rock Roses or Gum Cistus. In New Zealand they are known as Gallipoli Roses because they were first grown there from seeds brought home by soldiers from World War I.

The two Palestinian species of *Cistus* are dark or grey-green shrubs, four or five feet in height with flowers ranging from white to various shades of purplish-pink. Some are very beautiful, but all are evanescent lasting only a few hours and certainly never more than a day, but they are borne in such profusion that the shrubs remain in blossom day after day for weeks on end. Most of the species produce some gum but the most prolific is said to be *C. villosus* which is widespread in Palestine where Dr Post recognized no fewer than four distinct forms. It seems probable that ladanum was first used in that part of the world. Dr Post also noticed that in country districts a kind of tea was brewed from the leaves of *C. villosus*.

In early times ladanum was collected by herdsmen who obtained it by combing the fleeces of their flocks. Herodotus, writing about the middle of the fifth century B.C. says, 'Ladanum, which the Arabs call labdanum, is found in a most incongruous place. It is the sweetest of scented substances. It is gathered from the beards of he-goats, where it is found sticking like gum, having come from the bushes on which they browse. It is used in many sorts of unguents, and is what the Arabs burn chiefly as incense.'

The changing centuries brought greater demands and different ways of collecting ladanum. An old eighteenth-century botany book records that 'Ladanum is collected by means of an instrument called a ladanistrion which looks like a hay-rake whose teeth have been replaced by leather thongs. It is used like a whip to bruise the cistus bushes and the resin gathered by the thongs is scraped off with a knife.' Nowadays we know that the ladanum is secreted by glandular hairs on the leaves and young shoots and this knowledge has led to an entirely new method of extraction. The young tops are gathered and placed in vats where the ladanum is extracted by being dissolved in alcohol.

Ladanum, with its fragrance somewhat reminiscent of ambergris, is still of some commercial value. It is used in the preparation of wound dressings, plasters and other minor medicinal appliances, and also as a fixative in some of the cheaper scents, perfumed soaps and cosmetics. It is a far cry from the days when the Ishmaelites came down from Gilead carrying their 'myrrh' into Egypt, to the cake of scented soap in the modern bathroom, but *Cistus salvifolius* and *C. villosus* bridge the centuries.

MYRTLE

MYRTUS COMMUNIS

NEHEMIAH 8: 15

And that they shall publish and proclaim in all their cities, and in Jerusalem, saying, Go forth unto the mount, and fetch olive branches and pine branches, and myrtle branches and palm branches, and branches of thick trees, to make booths, as it is written.

ISAIAH 41: 19

I will plant in the wilderness the cedar, the shittah tree, and the myrtle, and the oil tree; I will set in the desert the fir tree, and the pine, and the box tree together.

ZECHARIAH 1: 8

I saw by night, and behold a man riding upon a red horse, and he stood among the myrtle trees that were in the bottom; and behind him were there red horses, speckled, and white.

MYRTLE

MYRTUS COMMUNIS

THE MYRTLE HAS NEVER BEEN OF ANY ECONOMIC IMPORTANCE, BUT ON ACCOUNT OF its pleasing appearance and scented blossom has been associated with peace, love and immortality since far back in the history of mankind. The Arabs say it was one of the three plants Adam chose to take with him on his way out of the Garden of Eden, chosen because it has the most fragrant of flowers. In Palestine it is commonly met with along the coast and, associated with the Sweet Bay and the Arbutus, in thickets alongside the streams that water the upland valleys.

In classical mythology the Myrtle was dedicated to Venus and her grove of Myrtle trees at Cnydos was set in a park containing plane and cypress trees, a place of great beauty in the days of long ago. An echo of this old association continues to this day when sprigs are being entwined among bridal flowers as 'an emblem of good luck'. Myrtle leaves were included in the laurel chaplets ceremoniously placed on the heads of poets and heroes as a token of triumph and respect.

In Biblical times the Myrtle was associated with the peace of the Lord and especially with the Feast of the Tabernacle. It was used in the observation of the original feast in 445 B.C. and has been used in the same manner ever since. Then, as now, an atmosphere of peace and goodwill filled the air while the children of Israel sat in myrtle groves, or, if that were not possible, in small arbours of green branches erected on the flat roofs of their houses.

Like most other plants that have been associated with man over a long period, the Myrtle has been put to many uses at one time or another. The delicate scent that is so characteristic of the finest Turkish leather has been absorbed through its being tanned with the roots and bark of myrtle. The dark blue fruits, sweet and aromatic, have long been used as a condiment, both fresh and dried, and an essential oil expressed from the plant is used in perfumery.

OLIVE

OLEA EUROPEA

GENESIS 8: 11

And the dove came to him in the evening; and, lo, in her mouth was an olive leaf pluckt off: so Noah knew that the waters were abated from off the earth.

DEUTERONOMY 24: 20

And when thou beatest thine olive tree thou shalt not go over the boughs again; it shall be for the stranger, for the fatherless, for the widow.

II SAMUEL 15: 30

And David went up by the ascent of Mount Olivet, and wept as he went up, and had his head covered, and he went barefoot.

LUKE 22: 39

And he came out and went, as he was wont, to the Mount of Olives: and his disciples also followed him.

OLIVE

OLEA EUROPEA

THE MOUNT OF OLIVES WHERE DAVID MOURNED OVER ABSALOM AND WHERE, A thousand years later, Jesus 'was wont to go'; the Garden of Gethsemane at its foot 'over the brook Cedron', appear, with the exception of a few surface changes, to be very much the same to-day as they were in Biblical times. Gethsemane, the place of the oil presses, was not a garden in the modern sense but an olive orchard where the trees grew thick and unpruned and where people could retire to enjoy their grateful shade, away from the heat of the noon-day sun. Such tree gardens are still common enough in the Near East; roughly enclosed by stone walls or thick, informal hedges, many have fig trees planted in the corners like the one mentioned in Luke 13.

Many of us would like to think that the olive trees of Gethsemane spring from the roots that grew there at the beginning of the Christian era. This is not altogether impossible, but two thousand years is a very long time. Contemporary historians record that the original trees were cut down by the Romans as part of the general destruction of the country after the fall of Jerusalem in A.D. 70, but this would not have killed the trees, and may, in fact, have rejuvenated them. When felled, olive tree stumps are capable of sending up strong saplings that will grow and take the place of the original trunks. Olives are said to live to an incredible age. Loudon, writing a hundred years ago, mentioned a plantation of olives, above two miles in extent, at Terne, near the cascade of Marmora in Italy saying they were referred to by Pliny in the middle of the first century A.D. If olive trees could live for nineteen hundred years in Italy there seems to be no reason why saplings which began life at the time of the fall of Jerusalem should not survive until our own time.

The olive has been cultivated for many long centuries and was so well known at the time of the flood, about 2347 B.C., that it could be recognized by a single leaf. The story of the dove and the olive has made a deep impression on mankind and everywhere they are accepted as the symbols of friendship and peace. In the course of the centuries new and better varieties were developed and increased to play their part in the story of mankind. It has been argued that 'the glory that was Greece' was founded on the humble olive tree. Improved forms gave ever better returns of oil, and these, in turn, brought riches and power and, with the help of slaves captured in war, the leisure that was to bring art and learning to such high achievement.

PALM

PHOENIX DACTYLIFERA

DEUTERONOMY 34: 3

And the south, and the plain of the valley of Jericho, the city of the palm trees, unto Zoar.

I KINGS 6: 29

And he carved all the walls of the house round about with carved figures of cherubims and palm trees and open flowers, within and without.

JOHN 12: 13

Took branches of palm trees, and went forth to meet him, and cried, Hosanna: Blessed is the King of Israel that cometh in the name of the Lord.

PALM

PHOENIX DACTYLIFERA

THE EMBLEM OF VICTORY, BEAUTY AND ABUNDANCE, THE DATE PALM HAS BEEN associated with the Levant since remotest antiquity. Phoenicia, the land of the Date Palms, was a rich and prosperous country whose main ports, Tyre and Sidon, were the great commercial centres of the ancient world. The many references in the Bible, from Elim,—the oasis where three score and ten palms marked the twelve wells,—right through to Revelations show that Palm trees were far more plentiful then than they are to-day. They were still so typical of the land in Roman times that a coin depicting a weeping woman beneath a palm was issued in Rome to celebrate the fall of Jerusalem.

The Palm has been cultivated for so long by the human race, following the westward course of civilization, that its original home is unknown but some authorities believe it originated somewhere between western India and the Gulf of Persia. Able to withstand the broiling heat of the sun and the cold, sometimes frosty, nights of the desert, the palm must always have a plentiful supply of water and that is why it is always to be found by rivers and lakes, overshadowing the wells, or marking the course of underground runnels.

The tree takes about forty years to reach maturity and by that time it may be more than a hundred feet in height, tall and graceful. It may bear crops for about 150 years after which a slow decline sets in. An interesting thing about these palms is that the male or pollen-bearing trees are distinct from the female or fruiting trees and only small crops may be expected if Nature is allowed to take her course. But, as many ancient Assyrian bas-reliefs and Egyptian inscriptions show, man has long since learned how to help things along by tying sprays of pollen-bearing flowers among the fruiting branches. Theophrastus, the Greek botanist who lived in the days of Alexander the Great knew the necessity for this and gave directions showing how it should be done, although he may not have understood the principles involved. Two thousand years later Parkinson, who was Apothocarie to James I scoffed at him and solemnly declared, 'The ancient writers have set down many strange things of the Dates; that they be male and female and that they beare fruit so that they be within sight of each other, or else they will not beare, but I pray you account this with the rest of their fables.'

ROSE OF SHARON

NARCISSUS TAZETTA

SONG OF SOLOMON 2: 1, 2

I am the rose of Sharon and the lily of the valleys. As a lily among thorns, so is my love among the daughters.

ISAIAH 35: 1

The wilderness and solitary place shall be glad for them; and the desert shall rejoice, and blossom as the rose.

Plate 10. ROSE OF SHARON. *Narcissus tazetta*
Painted by FERDINAND LUKAS BAUER
SIBTHORPE & SMITH: *Flora Graeca. Vol. IV.*

ROSE OF SHARON

NARCISSUS TAZETTA

THERE HAS BEEN MUCH DIFFERENCE OF OPINION ABOUT THE TRUE IDENTITY OF THE various 'roses' mentioned in the Bible and almost the only point upon which the various authorities agree is, that several very different plants have been loosely referred to under this name. When botanists took up the task of identifying the plants of the Bible they found themselves in difficulties because it soon became apparent that the early translators were interested in theology, and the spiritual message, and were quite indifferent as to whether or not the plant chosen to illustrate a point was, in fact, a lily or rose, or anything else.

The saying of Isaiah, ' ... the desert shall blossom as the rose', has passed into common speech and is a very good case in point. There is not a shadow of a clue, however, that the plant referred to is one of the wild roses of Palestine. Attractive enough in their own way, they are of no special beauty and are not at all likely to attract attention. As a matter of fact, the word translated as 'rose' in our own familiar version of the Bible has been variously rendered as lily, crocus and narcissus in other translations and modern opinion favours narcissus.

The common Polyanthus Narcissus is plentiful in Palestine and one of the joys of springtime. In the autumn the tender green shoots begin to peer through the dusty ground and, at the first touch of the winter rains, grow apace and send forth their fragrant blossoms in a very short time. The beauty of the Narcissus has been celebrated in song and story from time immemorial. Homer sang of it in his Hymn to Demeter:—

'The Narcissus wondrously glittering, a noble sight for all, whether immortal Gods or mortal men; from whose root a hundred heads spring forth, and at the fragrant odour thereof all the broad heaven above, and all the earth laughed, and the salt waves of the sea.'

ROSE OF THE BROOK—
OLEANDER OR ROSE LAUREL
NERIUM OLEANDER

WISDOM OF SOLOMON 2: 8

Let us crown ourselves with rose-buds, before they be withered.

ECCLESIASTICUS 39: 13

Hearken unto me, ye holy children, and bud forth as a rose growing by the brook of the field.

ECCLESIASTICUS 50: 8

And as the flower of roses in the spring of the year, as lilies by the rivers of waters, and as the branches of the frankincense tree in the time of summer.

Plate 11. ROSE OF THE BROOK. *Nerium oleander*
Painted by FERDINAND LUKAS BAUER
SIBTHORPE & SMITH; *Flora Graeca. Vol. III.*

ROSE OF THE BROOK—OLEANDER OR ROSE LAUREL

NERIUM OLEANDER

THE OLEANDER, OR ROSE LAUREL AS IT IS SOMETIMES CALLED, FLOURISHES SO LUXURIANTLY in Palestine that its beauty is one of the delights of the country. It is essentially a water-side plant and is especially plentiful by the margins of the lakes and along the banks of the brooks and streams of the Jordan valley. It flowers throughout the year with only a slight rest during the winter and there can be little doubt that it is the plant referred to in the passages we have quoted.

The pink, or rarely white, flowers grow like flat little roses in clusters at the ends of the branches while the leathery, evergreen leaves are said to be poisonous to stock. The Oleander is usually a shrub of only ten or twelve feet, but under very favourable conditions may become an elegant small tree with a trunk the thickness of a man's body. During the summer the flowering branches may be weighed down, like the long slim boughs of a weeping willow, with the abundance of their blossom.

In places where the fragrant Myrtle is not to be found the Oleander is very popular for making those temporary shelters used in the observance of the Jewish Feast of the Tabernacles. The leaves, tough and tenacious, have their pores set in depressions on the undersides and protected by microscopic hairs as a precaution against the excessive loss of moisture by drying winds, and so they last for several weeks without withering or falling off.

Few travellers who visit the Near East fail to comment on the beauty of the Oleanders, but no one has paid them finer tribute than C. M. Doughty. Of the bleak countryside around the Thorryid Passage in his *Travels in Arabia Deserta* he says, 'I saw nowhere the rose-laurel, whose blossoming thickets are the joy of our eyes in all fresh sites of limestone wilderness towards Syria. Beautiful at Petra, how beautiful in the torrents of Jordan!—and those wild gardens of exceeding beauty where of old stood the town of Caesarea Philippi,—But oh, the delicious groves of water blossom which blow by that blissful strand of the Lake of Galilee! Who that was a Christian, should not remember them in his grave, if that were possible.'

SAFFRON

CROCUS SATIVUS

Song of Solomon 4: 13, 14

Thy plants are an orchard of pomegranates with pleasant fruits; camphire with spikenard.
Spikenard and saffron, calamus and cinnamon, with all trees of frankincense, myrrh and aloes, with all the chief spices.

Plate 12. SAFFRON. *Crocus sativus*

Painted by PIERRE REDOUTÉ

REDOUTE; *Les Liliacees. Vol. III.*

SAFFRON
CROCUS SATIVUS

THE ORIGIN OF THIS PRETTY LITTLE AUTUMN-FLOWERING CROCUS IS SOMETHING OF A mystery. No one knows where it came from nor where it first began to be cultivated, but it has been known and valued for more than 3,500 years. In an old Theban papyrus believed to have been written in 1553 B.C. saffron, sesame, carraway and coriander figure among the medicinal herbs that have been identified with certainty. So there can be no doubt that the little flower with its brightly coloured stigma is the same saffron as grew in Solomon's garden.

The saffron of commerce consists of the stigmas, fragrant and thread-like, of this and a few allied species that grow wild in the Near East, but the best quality has always been obtained from the plant we know as *Crocus sativus*. This plant has not been known to set fertile seed which leads us to believe that it is of hybrid origin. Probably it first appeared among cultivated plants and in course of time increased and spread far and wide over the ancient world. Pliny writing in the first century A.D. tells us that 'Saffron loves to be beaten and trodden underfoot, and in fact, the worse it is treated the better it thrives'. This may mean that the corms were deliberately injured so that they would produce off-sets, because these are the only method of increase.

Saffron is still cultivated in various parts of the world, the best modern product being exported from Spain and Persia. Probably its main use nowadays is in colouring and flavouring foodstuffs and confections, but there was a time when saffron was listed among the most precious of the spices. In the fourth century A.D. the Emperor Constantine sent the Bishop of Rome a present of spices including saffron, cloves and pepper. But its uses have always been many and varied. In mediaeval Europe it was a very important article of commerce being used to scatter over the floors of royal audience chambers, in theatres and wherever people gathered, and of course it has been used as a dye for untold centuries.

One of the most astonishing things about the saffron trade was where the supply came from because over 4,000 stigmas are required for one ounce of the dry, raw product. In those days English saffron had a very high reputation and a romantic story is told of its arrival in England. 'A pilgrim, proposing to do good to his countrey, stole a head of saffron, and hid the same in his Palmer's staffe, which he made hollow before of purpose, and so he brought the roots into this realme with venture of his life, for if he had been taken, by lawe of the countrey from whence it came, he had died for the fact.' Such is supposed to have been the origin of the industry that gave its name to Saffron Walden where it flourished for 500 years, but this, the only record, was written by Hakluyt in 1582 some 350 years after it is supposed to have happened.

SYCAMORE

FICUS SYCOMORUS

II Chronicles 1: 15

And the king made silver and gold at Jerusalem as plenteous as stones, and cedar trees made he as the sycamore trees that are in the vale for abundance.

Psalms 78: 47

He destroyed their vines with hail, and their sycamore trees with frost.

Amos 7: 14

Then answered Amos, and said to Amaziah, I was no prophet, neither was I a prophet's son; but I was a herdsman, and a gatherer of sycamore fruit.

SYCAMORE
FICUS SYCOMORUS

THE SYCAMORE FIG HAS BEEN AN IMPORTANT ARTICLE OF FOOD AMONG THE POOR people of the Near East since the very dawn of civilization. The sweet fruit, smaller than the common fig and of poor quality, produced throughout the greater part of the year and in great abundance, grows on short leafless twigs that spring from the trunk and main branches. No one who can afford anything better will eat Sycamore Figs and poor indeed are those whose living depends on such a humble crop and so Amos was describing himself as the poorest of men when he told the king that he was 'a herdsman and a gatherer of sycamore fruit'.

Usually evergreen, the tree will drop its leaves during the coldest part of the year where conditions are not to its liking, but it will not stand frost. One of the greatest calamities that overcame the Egyptians was to have their sycamore trees destroyed by frost and this must be a very rare occurrence in that warm country. The leaves are somewhat heart-shaped and smaller than those of the common fig, and they are not lobed. Many authorities believe that it was these leaves which Adam and Eve used to make themselves aprons. The soft, porous wood is remarkably durable and seems to have been preferred by the ancient Egyptians for making their mummy cases, some of which have been found in excellent condition after a lapse of more than 3,000 years.

The Sycamore has a remarkable reputation for longevity and it is said that 'the Virgin's Tree' growing in the small village of Matariya, a few miles from Cairo goes right back to the beginning of the Christian era. According to tradition the Holy Family rested under this tree and took water from the nearby well during the flight to Egypt. A recent visitor says the tree 'grows inside a walled enclosure and holds one in awe with its appearance of extreme old age. Most of it seems to be a tangle of dead, gnarled branches covered with aged greenish-white bark, but there is one great branch which rises proudly above the confused mass waving its leaves and fruit with an air of triumph. Two or three hundred years ago this must have been a young sapling, but it too is showing signs of age although it seems to be defying the future and challenging time.'

It may be that the Virgin's Tree of Matariya has given its name to all the sycamores of the northern hemisphere, the wild Sycamore of England which is the Plane Tree of Scotland, and the Sycamores of North America. In olden times miracle plays were an easy method of teaching Bible stories to illiterate people and the Flight into Egypt was a favourite theme because few properties were required. During the journey the Holy Family rested under the Sycamore by the well at Matariya and because there were no real sycamore figs growing in England the local tree was chosen to fill the part, just as willows were used to take the place of palms on Palm Sunday. In both cases the name stuck and was accepted as the only one.

VINE

VITIS VINIFERA

JUDGES 9: 12, 13

Then said the trees unto the vine, Come thou, and reign over us.
And the vine said unto them, Should I leave my wine, which cheereth God and man, and go to be promoted over the trees?

EZEKIEL 18: 2

What mean ye, that ye use this proverb concerning the land of Israel, saying, The fathers have eaten sour grapes, and the children's teeth are set on edge?

JOHN 15: 5

I am the vine, ye are the branches: He that abideth in me, and I in him, the same bringeth forth much fruit: for without me ye can do nothing.

VINE

VITIS VINIFERA

GRAPE SEEDS FOUND NEARBY THE SITES OF STONE AGE DWELLINGS IN MANY PARTS OF Europe testify that vines were spread far and wide by primitive man at the very beginning of civilization. Dr Post in his investigations into the flora of Palestine and adjoining lands, found it 'cultivated everywhere in numerous varieties, but nowhere spontaneous', and came to the conclusion that 'its home is between the southern shores of the Caspian Sea and the Taurus.' We are never likely to know when or where Man first discovered that the fermented juice of grapes could exhilarate him as he had never been exhilarated before, but we can imagine that the plant capable of producing such magic would be eagerly sought after, and would be cherished above all others.

From time immemorial the grape harvest has been a season of laughter and happiness. In 1206 B.C. the Jews 'went out into the fields and gathered their vineyards, and trod the grapes and made merry.' Judges 9: 27. Then, as now, the harvest culminated in carnival, a celebration in honour of Bacchus, the god of wine, that was already old when the Jews were enduring their captivity in Babylon. In II Maccabees 6: 7, they complain bitterly because 'when the feast of Bacchus was kept, they were compelled to go in procession to Bacchus carrying ivy', giving an amusing picture of a company of indignant Jews, stalking along and casting sour looks on the ungodly while they carried sprays of ivy. There are more than 200 references to vineyards and their attendants, vines, grapes, raisins, wine and vinegar in the Bible. Wine drinking is taken for granted, but its excessive use is deplored and condemned by the prophets. The first thing Noah did when he came to set things to rights after the Flood was to become 'a husbandman and plant his vineyard'. Who can blame him if in after years he, missing the friends of his youth, 'drank of the wine and was drunken'.

The vine, along with the fig and the olive, was of such basic importance as to be accepted as a symbol of peace and plenty,—'But they shall sit, every man under his vine and under his fig tree: and none shall make them afraid.' Micah 4:4. It was to be one of the blessings of the Promised Land,—'a land of wheat and barley, and vines and fig trees.' Deut. 8: 8. and because of these oft-repeated promises came to be the emblem of the nation. 'Thou hast brought a vine out of Egypt: thou hast cast out the heathen and planted it.' Psalms 80: 8. Christ likened himself to a vine,—'I am the true vine, and my Father is the husbandman', and for this reason it came to be the emblem of the Christian Church.

In Numbers 13 we are told of the Jewish spies who 'came to the brook of Eschol, and cut from thence a branch with one cluster of grapes and they bare it between them upon a staff'. Many strange things have been written of this bunch of grapes, some writers going so far as to suggest that it must have been a bunch of bananas. There is a variety known as 'White Syrian', and one cannot help thinking that the name has some significance, said to be very old, which has the reputation of normally producing bunches of grapes ten pounds or more in weight. Clusters of 'White Syrian' weighing up to twenty pounds have been shown in horticultural shows in London and Loudon reports that it will produce clusters forty pounds in weight in well-irrigated land in Syria. The berries are large, coarse and of poor flavour and it is seldom grown nowadays. Taking all this into consideration there is nothing fantastic in two men carrying a large bunch of grapes 'between them on a staff'.